MINISTRY OF AGRICULTURE, FISHERIES AND FOOD

Food Standards Committee
Second Report
on Food Labelling

FSC/REP/69

LONDON

HER MAJESTY'S STATIONERY OFFICE

Recommendations relating to claims and misleading descriptions
are contained in the Food Standards Committee Second Report
on Claims and Misleading Descriptions

ISBN 0 11 240344 1

FOOD STANDARDS COMMITTEE

The terms of reference of the Food Standards Committee are:

To advise the Minister of Agriculture, Fisheries and Food, the Secretary of State for Social Services, the Secretary of State for Wales, the Secretary of State for Scotland and the Head of the Department of Health and Social Services for Northern Ireland, on the composition, description, labelling and advertising of food with particular reference to the exercise of powers conferred on Ministers by Sections 4, 5 and 7 of the Food and Drugs Act 1955 and the corresponding provisions in enactments relating to Scotland and Northern Ireland.

The following served on the Food Standards Committee during the preparation of this report:

Professor A G WARD, CBE, MA, F Inst P, FIFST, FAIFST (Chairman)
Professor R F CURTIS, BSc, PhD, DSc, FRIC, FIFST *(Deputy Chairman)*
Professor R J L ALLEN, OBE, MSc, PhD
M A CHAPMAN, MBE, FITSA, MBIM
J G COLLINGWOOD, DSc (Hon), BSc, C Eng, FI Chem E
R A DALLEY, M Chem A, C Chem, FRIC, FIFST
H EGAN, BSc, PhD, DIC, C Chem, FRIC, FRSH, FIFST
W P T JAMES, MA, MD, FRCP (from September 1978)
MRS C MCMASTER, FAHE
The late J A O'KEEFE, OBE, BSc (Econ), LLB, Barrister at Law, FITSA
R PASSMORE, MA, MD, FRCP (EDIN)
MRS G L S PIKE, CBE, JP
MISS R STEPHEN, MBE
F WOOD, MBE, BSc, C Eng, FI Chem E, FIFST

The following served as expert assessor on claims:

W P T JAMES, MA, MD, FRCP (until August 1978)

Joint Secretaries

MRS A M WATERS (until September 1978)
H B BROWN (from October 1978 until April 1979)
J A BAMFORD (from May 1979)
J R PARK, BSc, PhD (until October 1976)
I M V ADAMS, ANCFT, MFC, FIFST (from November 1976)

CONTENTS

I. INTRODUCTION

Scope of review

1.   In January 1975 we were asked by Ministers 'to review the labelling and advertising of food with reference to the provisions of the current regulations and of proposals for the harmonisation of legislation of Member States of the European Communities and to make recommendations'. This was to be the first full review of food labelling since our review of the Labelling of Food Order, 1953, discussed in our 1964 Report on Food Labelling[1] and our 1966 Report on Claims and Misleading Descriptions [2]. Following the announcement of the review we received detailed representations from over ninety interested organisations and individuals. Many additional representations were requested and received during the course of the review. All the organisations and individuals from whom representations have been received are listed at Appendix 1.

2.   Since our last review there have been extensive changes in food technology and marketing. Attitudes to food legislation have been changing, in part due to greater consumer interest in the United Kingdom, but also as a consequence of the United Kingdom becoming a Member State of the European Economic Community. The recommendations in this Report reflect the need thus created for changes in legislation affecting the United Kingdom, which will build on the firm foundations laid by existing labelling legislation. The changes which have taken place since our last review have also necessitated the establishment of general principles for food labelling: these general principles are discussed in paragraph 27 below.

Background

3.   Legislation based on the main recommendations in our 1964 Report on Food Labelling was enacted as the Labelling of Food Regulations 1967[3], the Coffee and Coffee Product Regulations 1967[4], the Ice-Cream Regulations 1967[5] and the Margarine Regulations 1967[6]. The 1967 Labelling of Food

---

[1]Food Standards Committee Report on Food Labelling: HMSO 1964.

[2]Food Standards Committee Report on Claims and Misleading Descriptions: FSC/REP/50: HMSO 1966.

[3]England and Wales SI 1967 No 1864
Northern Ireland SR & O (NI) 1968 No 1
There are no equivalent Scottish Regulations

[4]England and Wales SI 1967 No 1865   } To be superseded on 12 July 1980 by the
Scotland SI 1970 No 1284 (S103)   Coffee and Coffee Products Regulations 1978
There are no equivalent   (England and Wales SI 1978 No 1420
Northern Ireland Regulations   Northern Ireland SR & O (NI) 1979 No 51.
                                                         There are no equivalent Scottish Regulations)

[5]England and Wales SI 1967 No 1866
Scotland SI 1970 No 1285 (S104)
Northern Ireland SR & O (NI) 1968 No 13

[6]England and Wales SI 1967 No 1867
Scotland SI 1970 No 1286 (S105)
Northern Ireland SR & O (NI) 1968 No 3

Regulations, which came into operation in January 1968 but only in so far as they applied to foods (other than soft drinks) containing cyclamates, were however revoked by the Labelling of Food Regulations 1970, as amended[7], before they could come into force in other respects. The 1970 Labelling of Food Regulations, which re-enacted most of the labelling provisions of the 1967 Labelling of Food Regulations, contain in addition provisions relating to claims based on the recommendations in our 1966 Report on Claims and Misleading Descriptions. The length of the 1970 Labelling of Food Regulations makes reproduction of the full text in this Report impracticable. Appropriate references to the Regulations are however included in the text as necessary.

4.   The 1970 Labelling of Food Regulations superseded the Labelling of Food Order 1953, as amended[8], on 1 January 1973. Their operation has been generally effective and they are regarded as being successful both by consumers and the food industry. In Autumn 1974 however the Commission of the European Communities published preliminary proposals for a food labelling directive as an important part of the Community's food law harmonisation programme. Following detailed discussions among Member States, a Directive 'on the approximation of the laws of the Member States relating to the labelling, presentation and advertising of foodstuffs for sale to the ultimate consumer'[9] was adopted by the EEC Council of Ministers on 18 December 1978 and notified to Member States on 22 December 1978. The text of the Directive is reproduced at Appendix 3. We subsequently refer to the Directive in this Report as 'the EEC Food Labelling Directive'. In addition, in December 1976 the Council of Ministers adopted a Directive 'on Foods for Particular Nutritional Uses'[10] which, when implemented, will have an important bearing on the labelling of foods for which certain nutritional claims are made.

5.   The EEC Food Labelling Directive requires that after 22 December 1980 Member States must permit trade in products complying with the Directive and after 22 December 1982 they must prohibit trade in products not complying. Because of the limited time available, it is intended that proposals for UK implementing legislation will be issued as soon as possible to allow the

---

[7]England and Wales SI 1970 No 400 as amended by SI 1972 No 1510, SI 1974 No 1121, SI 1975 No 1485, SI 1976 No 509, SI 1976 No 541, SI 1976 No 859, SI 1976 No 1832, SI 1977 No 927, SI 1977 No 928, SI 1978 No 646 and SI 1978 No 1420.

Scotland SI 1970 No 1127 (S91) as amended by SI 1972 No 1790 (S141), SI 1974 No 1338 (SI16), SI 1975 No 1596 (S227), SI 1976 No 946 (S82), SI 1976 No 914 (S78), SI 1976 No 1176 (S102), SI 1976 No 1818 (S143), SI 1977 No 1026 (S79), SI 1977 No 1027 (S80) and SI 1978 No 927 (S78).

Northern Ireland SR & O (NI) 1970 No 80 as amended by SR & O (NI) 1972 No 318, SR (NI) 1974 No 196, SR & O (NI) 1975 No 275, SR (NI) 1976 No 165, SR (NI) 1976 No 183, SR (NI) 1976 No 212, SR (NI) 1976 No 387, SR (NI) 1977 No 182, SR (NI) 1977 No 196, SR (NI) 1978 No 206 and SR & O (NI) 1979 No 51.

[8]SI 1953, No 536 as amended by SI 1953 No 1889, SI 1955 No 1900, SI 1958 No 717, SI 1959 No 471 and SI 1961 No 440. (The complete, fully amended text of this Order may be found at Appendix B to the 1964 Food Standards Committee Report on Food Labelling — see footnote 1).

[9]Council Directive 79/112/EEC OJ No L33 8.2.79.

[10]Council Directive 77/94/EEC OJ No L26 31.1.77.

maximum period for consultations with interested parties. To ensure that our recommendations relating to implementation of the Directive are available for use in these consultations at as early a stage as possible, we decided that the relevant recommendations arising from our review of food labelling should be issued now, before our work on all aspects has been completed. This Report therefore deals generally with food labelling and in particular with the effects on UK labelling legislation of the EEC Food Labelling Directive. In some instances we are not sure that the Directive will allow certain definitions and provisions contained in the 1970 Labelling of Food Regulations to stand. This has not, however, deterred us from expressing our views, notwithstanding that the inclusion of some particular requirements of the current Regulations in the implementing legislation may be in doubt. Other relevant matters are also discussed. Recommendations on claims and misleading descriptions will be dealt with in our further report to be entitled Second Report on Claims and Misleading Descriptions which will be published shortly.

6. Developments during the course of this review also necessitated the issuing of two short Reports before the major parts of our work had been completed. These were Part I of our review, dealing with the Use of Fructose in Foods Specially Prepared for Diabetics[11] and Part II, dealing with Exemptions from Ingredient Listing and Generic Terms[12]. We also issued a Report on the Change from Calorie to Joule in Food Energy Declarations[13]. The Report on Exemptions from Ingredient Listing and Generic Terms is set out at Appendix 2 and the other two Reports will form appendices to our Second Report on Claims and Misleading Descriptions.

Arrangement of the report

7. In this Report we first examine developments in the food industry and elsewhere which have taken place since our last review and which have affected food labelling and claims generally. This section should be regarded as an introduction to our Second Report on Claims and Misleading Descriptions as well as to the present Report. We then go on to discuss the requirements of the 1970 Labelling of Food Regulations relevant to this Report in the order in which they appear in the Regulations, and recommend changes to take account of the developments discussed. Aspects of labelling not covered by the Regulations are also discussed as appropriate, as are relevant provisions in other regulations, usually those referring to specific commodities. At each stage, the implications of the EEC Food Labelling Directive are considered in relation to desirable developments in UK food labelling. Note has also been taken of recommendations concerning labelling in those of our reviews which have not yet resulted in legislation. Our discussion of the various issues and

---

[11]Food Standards Committee Review of Food Labelling: Part I: The Use of Fructose in Foods Specially Prepared for Diabetics: FSC/REP/69A: MAFF 1977.

[12]Food Standards Committee Review of Food Labelling: Part II: Exemptions from Ingredient Listing and Generic Terms: FSC/REP/69B: MAFF 1977.

[13]Food Standards Committee Report on the Change from Calorie to Joule in Food Energy Declarations: FSC/REP/67: MAFF 1976.

our recommendations are set out in the remainder of this Report under the following broad headings, which constitute Parts II to VII of the Report:

II. Developments since the last labelling review.
III. General labelling requirements.
IV. Specific labelling requirements for particular foods.
V. Manner of marking.
VI. Fish names.
VII. Miscellaneous matters.

A list of the recommendations in this Report and those in the Report on Ingredient Listing and Generic Terms (reproduced at Appendix 2) is given in Part VIII, paragraph 251.

II. DEVELOPMENTS SINCE THE LAST LABELLING REVIEW

Developments affecting labelling and claims generally

8. With the coming into operation of the 1970 Labelling of Food Regulations, consumers were provided with more specific and detailed information about the food they bought. Previous legislation (the 1953 Labelling of Food Order) had required prepacked food, other than intoxicating liquor, consisting of more than one ingredient to be identified by the common or usual name (if any). Many foods, in particular those for which there was a compositional regulation, were not required to list ingredients. In addition, a registered trade mark was allowed in place of the name and address of the packer or labeller. The 1970 Labelling of Food Regulations, however, require that almost all prepacked and much non-prepacked food be identified by an appropriate designation or common or usual name. A much greater number of prepacked foods must now carry a list of ingredients and almost all must bear the name and address of the packer or labeller on the label. The application of the 1970 Regulations is therefore more comprehensive and the requirements more detailed than the 1953 Order and since 1973, when the whole of the 1970 Regulations came into operation, consumers have had a much better opportunity to learn about and understand the nature of the food they buy. But, having established greater protection for the consumer, it is essential that this protection should be regularly and critically examined in the light of developments in the food industry (such as, for example, in relation to the introduction of novel protein foods and to the use of 're-formed' meat) and also of consumer expectation, to ensure that the requirements for food labelling are always such as to enable the consumer to make a sound and well-informed choice. The maintenance of effective and comprehensive food labelling laws is essential if this is to be achieved.

9. The variety of all types of foods available in the shops today has increased since our last review. The modern consumer is now presented with a greater diversity of foods from which to choose ranging from so-called 'convenience foods', which only became possible by the use of modern processing techniques, to the more traditional products such as meat pies, butter and cheese. Expansion of food production in other countries for export and developments in the storage and transportation of food have also meant that some foods, such as fresh fruit and vegetables, are available for much longer periods during the year. The reliance, for example, on canned or dried fruit and canned, dried or salted vegetables at certain times of the year, because of the absence of fresh supplies in the shops, is now greatly reduced. Frozen vegetables have however provided a processed product often closely matching high quality fresh produce. The increasing availability of foods based on foreign cuisines, particularly Chinese and Indian dishes, whether in restaurants, 'take-away' establishments or prepacked from supermarket shelves, has broadened consumers' tastes and their willingness to experiment with unfamiliar foods. Although there has been an apparent increase in the

number of different brands of foods available the choice to the consumer may in fact have diminished because an increasing number of retail shops have tended to concentrate on the sale of so-called 'own-label' products. We are not sure of how far the public is aware how rarely 'own-label' means 'own-manufacture'. We understand that some supermarkets display only their 'own-label' plus the brand leader of some foods, preferring not to take up shelf-space with other less saleable brands of the same product. Indeed, some supermarkets sell only 'own-label' products.

10.   Developments in food technology have also played an important part in increasing the variety of foods available and in presenting and preparing foods in ways unfamiliar to the consumer. New processes such as sterilisation by ultra heat treatment (UHT) combined with aseptic packaging, improved drying techniques including freeze drying, and the use of new packaging materials such as laminated pouches (to replace the traditional can) are just some examples. Improvements in the refrigerated food chain have meant that a greater range of perishable foods can now be stocked by the retailer and such perishable foods can usually remain in the shops (and in the home) for longer periods without deterioration. These developments have resulted in processed foods, including bread, pasteurised milk and chill-stored or peeled fruit and vegatables, taking up a high and increasing proportion of the diet[14]. Long familiar foods such as ham have frequently been modified in some way to exploit new technological processes and, in the absence of a compositional standard, may have changed significantly in composition. Nevertheless, recent compositional standards have usually made some provisions for useful technological change. In these circumstances clear, accurate and positive labelling is especially important if the consumer is to be fully informed.

11.   Variations in the supply of raw materials and increases in their prices, rising energy costs and inflation generally have presented great difficulties for the manufacturer in trying to achieve a measure of price stability. At the same time, pressures from within the food trade such as intense competition and the purchasing power of supermarket chains have been reinforced by the actions of government in delaying or reducing price increases. All these factors have made it increasingly difficult for manufacturers to maintain the quality of their products.

12.   The particularly rapid rise in the cost of some ingredients has led to a reduction in their use, in order to keep price rises to a minimum. Where this cannot be done, for instance where there is a compositional standard controlling such ingredients, manufacturers may turn to sources not previously utilised. An example is mechanically recovered meat, which has been made available by technical developments to supplement former sources of meat for processing. Economic and other circumstances have also

---

[14]Consumption of foods subject to some degree of processing (excluding fresh fruit and vegetables) increased by nearly 12% between 1964 and 1977 (when measured at constant 1975 prices). These foods' share of total food consumption was 72% in 1977. Source: MAFF, unpublished.

influenced the use of techniques to increase the water content of some foods above that traditionally expected. The recommendations for the declaration of added water in our Report on Water in Food[15] and other measures proposed in that Report are intended to meet this particular problem. Where basic raw material or ingredient costs have risen significantly, 'substitute' products may have been developed. These may not be complete substitutes developed from totally different initial ingredients but may contain a smaller proportion of the expensive ingredient in combination with a cheaper one claimed to have similar properties. Wherever such factors have resulted in product changes, clear and informative labelling is essential if the consumer is not to be confused or misled.

13.   We would not wish to criticise the search for substitute and modified foods which are nutritionally adequate and safe to eat. Provided these foods are labelled, advertised and promoted for what they are, as required by law, there can be no objection to their sale. Indeed, it is our firm belief that controls imposed on food manufacturers should wherever possible be such that innovation and technological developments can still be used to full advantage for the benefit of both consumer and manufacturer. However, some of these developments could result in substandard versions of commonly known and well recognised foods. The existence of a compositional standard can protect against the abuse of an established food name but the proliferation of near alternatives not covered by the standard requires careful and distinct differentiation by clear and accurate labelling. Compositional standards do not necessarily achieve this because their scope is limited and the great variety of foods that are sold would make the imposition of compositional standards for all of them impracticable. Some foods, by their variable nature or because of their restricted place in the diet, would also make such universal control by composition inappropriate. Compositional standards are especially important for staple foods (such as bread and meat products) which are nutritionally significant in the national diet. If universal control were to be attempted, the amount of legislation necessary would clearly outweigh any resultant benefits. General food labelling requirements are the most effective form of overall control, supported by compositional and specific labelling requirements where the general provisions need to be supplemented.

14.   In addition to factual information given on labels such as the name of the food and the ingredients list, manufacturers often make claims about their products, whether in general terms such as 'our product is good' or in a more specific manner such as that it is rich in vitamin C or useful for a particular group of consumers such as diabetics. Such claims are the way in which manufacturers attempt to draw consumers' attention to particular aspects of their products or to the superiority of their products over those of their competitors. The claims made in advertisements in this respect can play an important part in influencing consumer choice. Providing these claims remain within the limits imposed by the existing general law as contained in the Food

---

[15]Food Standards Committee Report on Water in Food: FSC/REP/70: HMSO 1978.

and Drugs Acts[16] there can be little objection to most of them. But of particular concern are those claims relating to a specific aspect of a food which, because of their complexity, may be unsuitable for control solely by the general provisions of the Acts. There are also general claims where some of the terms used have become virtually meaningless either through over-use (eg 'new', 'improved') or by application in too widely differing circumstances (eg 'fresh'). The increasing sales of 'health foods' with their accompanying 'health' claims must also be of concern: we have been told that many of the claims now made for these foods appear not to comply with the existing law. At the same time a number of implied claims are made which may not be susceptible to existing legal controls.

15. Claims made for foods are not limited to words written on a label or spoken in an advertisement. Illustrations on labels and in advertisements exert a considerable influence. Visual impressions are particularly effective in television advertising. A claim can be implied by appropriate use of pictures and the 'product image' portrayed; it is this area which is particularly difficult to control.

16. A further, but no less important, development since the last review of food labelling is the general increase in consumer awareness and expectation discussed in paragraphs 8 and 9 of our Report on Ingredient Listing[17]. Consumer pressure has resulted in laws dealing with many aspects of consumer protection and the information available to and protection provided for consumers has consequently increased to a considerable extent.

17. We have examined the 1970 Labelling of Food Regulations to see whether consumer needs are fully and effectively provided for. The consumer requires, for example, to be given sufficient information to avoid possible confusion caused by sophisticated methods of marketing and to enable a fair choice to be made between different foods. Our recommendations for full ingredient listing in our Report on Ingredient Listing should help to achieve these objectives. While recognising the important contribution made by the 1970 Labelling of Food Regulations, we have concluded that the existing requirements should be strengthened in certain respects to ensure that developing consumer needs are met. In several of our Reports (Beer[18], Soft Drinks[19] and Novel Protein Foods[20]) we have recommended percentage declaration of the main or characterising ingredient as part of the description, although these recommendations have not so far been implemented. Such percentage declarations are probably best decided commodity by commodity rather than by a general regulation. We wish however to record our continuing

---

[16]Food and Drugs Act 1955; 4 Eliz. 2 C 16. Food and Drugs (Scotland) Act 1956; 4 & 5 Eliz. 2 C 30. Food and Drugs Act (Northern Ireland) 1958; C 27 (NI).

[17]For ease of reference in this Report, the Report on Exemptions from Ingredient Listing and Generic Terms will be referred to throughout as the 'Report on Ingredient Listing'.

[18]Food Standards Committee Report on Beer: FSC/REP/68: HMSO 1977.

[19]Food Standards Committee Review of the Soft Drinks Regulations 1964 (as amended) Part II Soft Drinks: FSC/REP/65: HMSO 1976.

[20]Food Standards Committee Report on Novel Protein Foods: FSC/REP/62 HMSO 1974.

view that percentage declarations, used specifically but sparingly, are a very effective means of informing consumers and enabling proper comparisons to be made.

18.   The recognition of consumer needs and the necessity for protection have also led to the development of codes of practice to regulate advertising: these codes are discussed in our Second Report on Claims and Misleading Descriptions.

Extension of the scope of labelling legislation

19.   In meeting the need for the consumer to be informed by labelling of the nature of food being purchased, past legislation and our own reviews have concentrated on prepacked food sold in a retail shop. However, there are two aspects of labelling which have been increasingly drawn to our attention. The first concerns food sold in catering premises, which include restaurants, canteens and sandwich bars, and the rapidly growing 'take away' sector. The information provided to consumers by caterers is frequently inadequate as a basis for choice and the information provided to the caterer by food manufacturers and distributors is also often inadequate. Food in or on a container does not fall within the definition of 'prepacked' in the 1970 Labelling of Food Regulations, quoted in paragraph 33, unless it is made up in advance ready for retail sale and the definition 'sell by retail', quoted in paragraph 35, excludes selling to a caterer for the purposes of his catering business. The provisions of the 1970 Regulations which apply to prepacked food therefore have no application when food packed in advance in or on a container is sold to a caterer. Similar exemptions for sales of food to caterers are incorporated in other regulations made under the Food and Drugs Acts eg those for butter, ice-cream, meat products and sausages. This means that a caterer may buy, without contravening the law, some foods which would be in breach of compositional requirements if sold by retail. These exemptions have been shown to be misguided. Caterers have expressed an interest in having the full protection of the law in the supply of information about the food they buy, in the same way as if purchased by retail. We discuss the possible extension of the scope of the labelling law as it affects the caterer in paragraphs 33, 34, 35 and 87 below. The withdrawal of all the exemptions from control at present applying to supplies to caterers, as mentioned above, is also important in relation to certain compositional standards.

20.   The second aspect of labelling drawn to our attention is the sale of non-prepacked foods. The 1970 Labelling of Food Regulations apply only to certain limited aspects of non-prepacked sales. It has been argued that the Regulations should apply equally to all non-prepacked as to prepacked foods since the consumer needs information about all foods purchased. Although there would be considerable practical difficulties in meeting such a requirement, we accept in principle that non-prepacked food should be accompanied by fuller information, especially concerning matters not evident to a prospective purchaser. We discuss in detail the extension of existing

9

labelling requirements to cover sales of non-prepacked foods in paragraphs 89-98 below.

The effects of EEC directives on UK food labelling law

21. UK membership of the European Economic Community represents a further significant change since our last review. The EEC Commission is engaged in harmonising the food laws of the Community. There are two main purposes in this, firstly a reduction in barriers to trade and secondly, the protection of the consumer, including increased provision of more uniformly displayed information. Food law harmonisation is mainly effected by directives rather than regulations, so that the Community rules may be written into the long established bodies of food legislation which exist in each of the Member States. No attempt can be made to harmonise the basic framework of the food law (such as that provided by the Food and Drugs Acts in the UK) as the national variations in approach are so great. Food law forms part of the general body of law in each country and so is affected by basic differences in the legal systems. However, some attempt can and is being made to provide, as early steps toward harmonisation, that in each country the same information about a food must be given, that food may contain only certain specified additives and that certain foods must comply with common compositional standards.

22. One of the directives seen by all concerned as of great importance in the harmonisation programme is the Food Labelling Directive, the provisions of which are set out at Appendix 3. Work on this Directive has taken place in parallel with our review. The difficulties inherent in securing Community agreement on all major and minor parts of so important an area of food legislation are acknowledged. On occasions little more can be achieved than a compromise between conflicting views, which themselves are based on national needs and national experience. But in contrast the whole Community may, without a dissenting voice, take a major step forward in its aim of increasing the information available for the consumer, such as requiring that all foods should bear a list of ingredients.

23. The rules imposed when a directive is agreed necessarily limit the freedom of action of Member States to regulate independently. The implementation of the EEC Food Labelling Directive will mean that a number of the widely accepted detailed rules in the 1970 Labelling of Food Regulations will no longer be permitted. The introduction of new national rules may also need to be delayed until they can be agreed on a Community basis. In some instances such a delay will not be to the advantage of the consumer. Legislation on the open date marking of food, for instance, has been deferred in the UK pending the agreement of the EEC Food Labelling Directive which contains date marking provisions. As long ago as 1972 we recommended in our Report on the Date Marking of Food[21] that a statutory system of open date marking should be introduced. Such a delay has not been to the advantage of

---

[21]Food Standards Committee Report on the Date Marking of Food: FSC/REP/59: HMSO 1972.

consumers seeking greater information about the food they buy. Indeed, for industry also it has greatly extended the period of uncertainty, as well as losing the impetus provided by the voluntary action of a number of manufacturers and distributors in introducing open date marking for certain commodities after publication of the Report. We would wish to see open date marking legislation introduced as quickly as possible and we hope that further delays will be minimized. We have not considered date marking as part of this review since its main features will be determined by the EEC Food Labelling Directive and we therefore make no further recommendations on the subject.

24.   The adoption of the EEC Directive on Foods for Particular Nutritional Uses will also have an important part to play in increasing information for consumers. Once implemented, the Directive will require more detailed information than at present on the labels of those foods for which certain nutritional claims are made and the provisions will supplement and enhance the existing requirements of the 1970 Labelling of Food Regulations. The detailed requirements of the Directive will be discussed in our Second Report on Claims and Misleading Descriptions.

Medicines legislation

25.   Another important development in consumer information since our last review has been the introduction of detailed labelling requirements for medicinal products. The Medicines Act 1968 and Regulations made under it specify, among other things, the information to be given on the labels of medicinal products sold as such and also those sold as foods. We discuss this legislation in relation to claims for foods in our Second Report on Claims and Misleading Descriptions.

The need for general labelling principles

26.   The changes in food production and marketing and in consumer attitudes which have taken place since our last review have led us to conclude that general guiding principles for food labelling need to be established. We appreciate that sucl. principles can only operate within the constraints now imposed by the EEC Food Labelling Directive but the implementation of the Directive into UK law will provide a useful opportunity for these general principles to be applied. Implementation of the Directive will not represent, in our view, a significant advance on the main provisions of the 1970 Labelling of Food Regulations except in respect of open date marking and the declaration of added water, but skilled drafting will be required to convert the Directive into UK law. Principles established by this Committee could have an important role to play in guiding that drafting. The discussions on these principles during our present review have assisted UK officials involved in negotiating the Labelling and some other Directives and the guiding principles should similarly aid future negotiations and EEC discussions. They will help all interested parties to understand more clearly the aims of labelling legislation and so stimulate constructive comment and discussion when future laws are proposed.

11

General labelling principles

27.   There can be no long term divergence of interest between consumers and the food trade, whatever short term disagreements may arise. Manufacturers must be able to satisfy the desires, preferences and nutritional needs of the consumer: the retailer's interest is served, in the long term, by enabling the consumer to be aware of what he or she is buying. The consumer is able to exercise the purchaser's right to buy or not to buy a particular food but is dependent on the skill of the manufacturer in preserving food for consumption when wanted and in increasing the attractiveness of preserved foods. Unless a general standard of honesty and intelligibility is maintained, the consumer will be misled and the honest trader prejudiced. In the light of the principles set out in our earlier Reports on Labelling and Claims, we therefore *recommend* that all future labelling legislation should be based on the following general principles:—

(a)   all food whether prepacked or non-prepacked should be identified in ways readily visible to the purchaser. This should apply whenever the food is sold and should no longer be restricted to retail sales. The only exception should be sales to a manufacturer for the purpose of his business;

(b)   food should be sold without deceit as to composition and character and should be so labelled as to enable a prospective purchaser to make a fair and informed choice based on clear and informative labelling;

(c)   established food names should be protected: debasement of accepted and common food names should be prevented;

(d)   pedantic detail and excessive labelling should be avoided as this may confuse or mislead the consumer.

(e)   pictures on labels, shapes of packages and the presentation of food may exert powerful influences on the prospective purchaser and should be considered as candidates for control in the same way as the words used on labels: indeed for some sectors of the population, they may have a greater significance than names and descriptive material;

(f)   legislation should protect both consumers and honest and diligent traders: it should allow fair comparison between products;

(g)   the interests of consumers should be paramount.

We have applied these general principles throughout our review. They have been expanded as necessary to deal with the particular subjects discussed.

III.   GENERAL LABELLING PROVISIONS

Read, mark, learn and inwardly digest

The Book of Common Prayer

28.   Parts I and II of the 1970 Labelling of Food Regulations set out general provisions relating to the labelling and advertising of food, including definitions of some of the terms used and certain exemptions from particular requirements. While all the provisions are applicable to labels, only certain ones apply to advertisements and we make this clear when discussing the relevant parts of the Regulations.

Definitions of terms (Regulations 2(1) to 2(6))

29.   With the exception of 'appropriate designation' (defined in Regulation 3), the principal terms used in the Regulations are defined in Regulations 2(1) to 2(6). The most important of these definitions are discussed in paragraphs 30-39 below.

30.   *'Container'* is defined as including:

'any form of packaging of food for sale as a single item, whether by way of wholly or partly enclosing the food or by way of attaching the food to some other article and in particular includes a wrapper or confining band, but does not include any open punnet, basket or similar container used for fresh fruit and vegetables or any crimp case used to support the base or the base and sides of flour confectionery, sugar confectionery, chocolate confectionery or chocolate products or any similar product partly or wholly encased in pastry if such a product has been subject to a baking or cooking process'.

This definition is adequate for virtually all food sold in some form of packaging and includes foods using the minimum of such materials such as watercress which may be sold by the bunch with a small confining band around the outside. This may, we are informed, be taken as a container for the purposes of the Regulations. There is no definition of 'container' in the EEC Food Labelling Directive, but the definition of 'pre-packaged foodstuff' (discussed in paragraph 34 below) refers to packaging which encloses food '. . . in such a way that the contents cannot be altered without opening or changing the packaging'. This definition would not appear to include the use of wrappers or confining bands if the contents can be altered without opening or changing such packaging. Some food packed in this way might thus in future be regarded as non-prepacked. It is important, however, that these types of packaging continue to be regarded as 'containers' for the purposes of food labelling legislation to avoid the possibility of abuse. We therefore hope that, under the provisions of legislation to implement the EEC Food Labelling Directive, wrappers and confining bands will continue to be regarded as containers for legislative purposes.

13

31.   It should be noted that open punnets, baskets, etc for fresh fruit and vegetables and crimp cases for certain types of confectionery (including flour confectionery) are not regarded as containers for the purposes of the 1970 Labelling of Food Regulations and hence do not have to be labelled in accordance with the Regulations. This exemption would seem to be fully justified in view of the practical labelling difficulties involved and because of the need to encourage the wrapping of food for hygienic purposes but without in so doing attracting onerous labelling requirements. We therefore *recommend* that the present exemptions continue. The precise form in which they can be included in future legislation does not seem to us to matter as long as the provision is effective and we accept that any future definition of 'container' may need to be different from the existing one because of the requirement to implement the EEC Food Labelling Directive.

32.   *'Food'* is defined as:

'food intended for sale for human consumption and includes:

(a)   cream and any food containing milk, and

(b)   drink, chewing gum and other products of a like nature and use, and articles and substances used as ingredients in the preparation of food or drink or of such products,

but does not include —

(i)   water, live animals or birds, or

(ii)   articles or substances used only as drugs'.

This definition is slightly different from, but not inconsistent with, the definition of 'food' in Section 135 of the Food and Drugs Act 1955. Both definitions will need to be examined in the light of the provisions of the Medicines Act 1968, which we will be discussing in our Second Report on Claims and Misleading Descriptions. The exclusion of water from the definition in the 1955 Act has been fully discussed in our 1978 Report on Water in Food. The 1955 Act and its Scottish and Northern Ireland counterparts are presently under review by Government Departments and the definitions in the Acts, including that of 'food', are being examined. We would only *recommend* here that consideration should be given to amending the definition to include water as a food so as to make clear that water behaves as a food in that it takes an active part in nutrition and is not merely a carrier for nutrients and metabolites. As such it should appear in the list of ingredients. This change is also needed to enable labelling regulations applicable to prepacked water (mineral water, etc) to be made under the Food and Drugs Acts.

33.   *'Prepacked'* is defined as:

'made up in advance in or on a container ready for sale by retail, save that in relation to any food with one main ingredient or to any flour confectionery, bread or sandwiches this expression means so made up in or on a container other than a wholly transparent container; and where

14

any food made up in or on a container is found on any premises where such food is so made up or is kept or stored for sale, that food shall be deemed to be prepacked unless the contrary is proved, and it shall not be sufficient proof of the contrary to show that the food had not been labelled in accordance with the provisions of these regulations'.

The use of the words '. . . . made up in advance in or on a container ready for sale by retail . . . .' ensures that to be regarded as prepacked under the 1970 Regulations food must have been packed or wrapped before sale in the shop. Accordingly the placing of food in a bag or wrapper by the retailer at the time of sale is not included but if this is done before the shop is open or for instance during the morning to cope with a sudden rush of customers at lunchtime, then the food is deemed to be 'prepacked' and must comply with any statutory requirements. The use of the words 'sale by retail' removes from the definition food in a container sold to a manufacturer as well as that sold to a caterer for the purposes of his catering business. The exemption for 'wholly transparent containers' from the definition of 'prepacked' is a sensible and logical attempt to ensure that the Regulations do not restrict the use of wrapping materials for hygienic purposes as discussed in paragraph 31 above. It is hoped, as stressed in paragraph 36 below, that the EEC Food Labelling Directive will permit these sensible provisions to continue.

34. The EEC Food Labelling Directive defines 'prepackaged foodstuff' as:

'any single item for presentation as such to the ultimate consumer, consisting of a foodstuff and the packaging into which it was put before being offered for sale, whether such packaging encloses the foodstuff completely or only partially, but in any case in such a way that the contents cannot be altered without opening or changing the packaging'.

With the exception of our doubts about the omission of explicit reference to the use of wrappers or confining bands (paragraph 30) and to the use of wholly transparent containers (paragraph 36), we consider that this definition is not inconsistent with the definition of 'prepacked' in the 1970 Labelling of Food Regulations. Like the definition in those Regulations, the definition in the Directive would not appear to apply to sales to caterers or manufacturers, being related to presentation of food 'to the ultimate consumer'. Article 1.2 of the Directive however permits Member States to apply the Directive to foods 'intended for supply to restaurants, hospitals, canteens and other similar mass caterers, insofar as the Member States shall so decide'. For reasons given in paragraphs 19 and 87, we *recommend* that the labelling provisions of the EEC Food Labelling Directive be applied to food sold to caterers.

35. *'Sell by retail'* is defined as:

'sell to a person buying otherwise than for the purpose of re-sale, but does not include selling to a caterer for the purposes of his catering business or to a manufacturer for the purposes of his manufacturing business; and 'sale by retail' and 'sold by retail' shall be construed accordingly'.

'Sell' includes 'offer or expose for sale or have in possession for sale, and

15

'sale' and 'sold' shall be construed accordingly'.

Apart from the unsatisfactory position concerning sales to caterers, both of these definitions have proved satisfactory in operation. If permitted by the EEC Food Labelling Directive, we *recommend* that the definition 'sell' be retained and, if our recommendation in paragraph 34 is accepted, that the definition 'sell by retail' is amended specifically to include selling to a caterer for the purposes of his catering business.

36.　*'Wholly transparent container'* as referred to in paragraph 33 is defined as:

> '......a container through which no portion of that part of the surface of the food which is naturally adjacent to the inner surface of the container is obscured from view; and includes any net or mesh bag or other similar bag through which the food can be clearly seen but does not include any container on which there is any written matter other than such as is necessary to indicate the price of the food, whether or not that written matter is transparent'.

We consider that, for the reasons given in paragraph 33, this exemption from the definition of 'prepacked' has an important role to play and we would wish to see it contained in any future legislation. We have been told however that the terms of the EEC Food Labelling Directive will probably not allow this important provision to continue although similar effect may be achieved by other exemptions. We *recommend* that if at all possible the effects of this valuable exemption should be included in any implementing legislation. If it were retained, we consider that, in addition to the price, the retailer's name and address and (to be consistent with Regulation 6(2) — see paragraph 77 below) the quantity of the food, should be permitted to appear on the container without the exemption being lost. If these last two are marked on the wrapper at present the food is no longer in a 'wholly transparent container' and has to comply fully with the requirements of the Regulations for prepacked foods.

37.　*'Label'* is not defined in detail but Regulation 2(3) refers to:

> 'any reference .... to a label borne on a container shall be construed as including a reference to any legible marking on the container however effected'.

For the purposes of future labelling legislation, this should be sufficient and we so *recommend*.

38.　*'Advertisement'* is not defined in the Regulations but, by virtue of Regulation 2(1), the definition in Section 135 of the Food and Drugs Act 1955 applies. We think that this is an important definition, covering as it does a wide variety of circumstances and we *recommend* that, for clarity, the following definition of 'advertisement' in Section 135 of the 1955 Act should be used in future legislation:

> ' 'Advertisement' includes any notice, circular, label, wrapper, invoice or

16

other document, and any public announcement made orally or by any means of producing or transmitting light or sound, and 'advertise' shall be construed accordingly'.

39. *Other interpretation provisions and definitions.* The remaining definitions and provisions in Regulations 2(1) to 2(6) do not appear to be causing any difficulties nor would they seem to be prohibited by the terms of the EEC Food Labelling Directive. We *recommend* their continued inclusion in legislation.

The appropriate designation definition (Regulation 3 and Schedule 1)

40. *Definition.* 'Appropriate designation' is defined in Regulation 3(1) as:

'. . . . . . a name or description or a name and description sufficiently specific, in each case, to indicate to an intending purchaser the true nature of the food to which it is applied and, as respects any ingredient or any constituent, a specific (and not generic) name or description which will indicate to an intending purchaser the true nature of the ingredient or constituent, as the case may be, to which it is applied'.

Names laid down in regulations for specified foods eg 'sausage', 'butter' are regarded as appropriate designations by virtue of Regulation 3(2) and names which have been in use throughout a period of at least 30 years before 4 January 1971 eg 'Oxo' are also regarded as appropriate designations provided they are not misleading (Regulation 3(4)): this latter provision is known as the 'thirty year rule'. Finally, Regulation 3(3) requires that where the names of two or more ingredients are used in the appropriate designation other than adjectivally, these names must be used in the order by weight in which they are used in the food (unless other regulations require otherwise) eg in a description such as 'sausages and beans', there must be a greater quantity of sausages than beans in the product. Where the names of two or more ingredients are used adjectivally in an appropriate designation, such as 'blackberry and apple pie', the order of the names must not be calculated to mislead as to the proportions of such ingredients used. This is to allow the characterising but smaller ingredients to appear first as in 'spiced apple tart'. Where a food is sold in a carrying liquor such as vinegar, brine, or syrup, the name of the food may precede the name of the liquor eg peaches in syrup.

41. It will be seen from the definition above that an appropriate designation of a *food* has to be only 'sufficiently specific . . . . to indicate to an intending purchaser the true nature of the food' whereas that for an *ingredient* must be 'a specific (and not generic) name or description . . . .'. In our 1964 Report on Food Labelling we said in paragraph 26 that 'true nature' means 'a clear and accurate description of the characteristics of the food or the ingredient' and we believe the appropriate designations given for both the food and the ingredients should be as specific as possible. However, where there are compositional regulations for particular foods or where a food is and has been commonly named in a particular way it has for long been recognised that names such as 'sausage', 'meat pie', 'cheese spread', 'tea' may be perfectly acceptable for the needs of the purchaser and it is left to the seller to be more

17

specific if he chooses. The words 'sufficiently specific' allow for such an exercise of judgement. The appropriate designation requirements for the food are sufficient to distinguish between foods of the same general type but with different characteristics such as thick and clear soups. Ingredients, on the other hand, by their very nature are more susceptible to precise definition and as such we think that the difference in requirements is justified. We consider that the existing definition in Regulation 3(1) is therefore satisfactory and *recommend* that it should be retained, subject to the amendment recommended in paragraph 42.

42. *Common or usual names.* As discussed in paragraph 50 below, the 1970 Regulations allow, for foods with more than one ingredient, the use of a 'common or usual name' in place of, and not as a form of, an appropriate designation. These are traditional names which are familiar to the public but which are not necessarily directly descriptive of the foods to which they are applied, such as 'Eccles cake', 'Bath bun', 'wine gums', 'barley sugar'. 'Common or usual name' is not defined in the present Regulations. We understand that this had led to enforcement difficulties in some instances where uninformative coined names of fairly recent invention have been claimed to be 'common or usual' names and have been given on labels in place of an appropriate designation. We would wish to see this area of imprecision removed from the Regulations and therefore *recommend* that the definition of 'appropriate designation' be amended to allow it to include a common or usual name, provided it is made clear that only a common or usual name that is sufficiently well established may be an appropriate designation, always providing that it is not misleading. This amendment would clarify the existing requirements and reduce the possibility of abuse. At the same time, common or usual names would be allowed to describe one ingredient foods which are not at present permitted to make use of this alternative. A more consistent approach to their use will therefore be achieved. We understand that our recommendations on the definition of 'appropriate designation' are consistent with the provisions of the EEC Food Labelling Directive. The definition in paragraph 40, as amended by the recommendation above on the use of common or usual names, is subsequently regarded in the text of this Report as defining the *appropriate designation* and where we use that term subsequently it should be construed in that sense.

43. *Names laid down by other regulations.* These names, whether linked to composition or not, are regarded as appropriate designations (Regulation 3(2)) and we consider that this operates satisfactorily as discussed in paragraph 40 above. There is a similar provision in the EEC Food Labelling Directive. We *recommend* that the provision be retained.

44. *Order of ingredients listed in the appropriate designation.* This is controlled successfully by Regulation 3(3) (see paragraph 40 above) and we *recommend* that there should be no change.

45. *The 'thirty-year rule'.* This rule is at present permitted by Regulation 3(4)

(see paragraph 40 above) and should no longer continue. We think it unlikely that products making use of the rule will have remained completely unchanged in formulation over the years and can therefore see no real objections to the labels of these foods being required to carry an appropriate designation in addition to the familiar brand name. Products with names often given as examples of '30 year' names may in fact already carry appropriate designations in addition to the brand name. The 'thirty year rule' would not in any event be permitted under Article 5.2 of the EEC Food Labelling Directive which forbids the use of a trade mark, brand name or fancy name in place of a name as prescribed in Article 5.1, but even were this not so we would *recommend* its demise.

46. *Appropriate designations for fish.* Appropriate designations for fish, both when sold prepacked and non-prepacked, are required by Regulation 3(5) and set out in Schedule 1. We have recommended a number of changes to the Schedule in Section VI (paragraphs 205-238) of this Report and a revised Schedule is set out at Appendix 4.

47. *Statements of purpose.* These are sometimes used as appropriate designations such as 'a mix for goulash' or 'coffee creamer'. Such descriptions do not indicate the 'true nature' of the food and are not in our view appropriate designations. They should always be accompanied by a correct designation. We fully appreciate the value of such statements to the consumer, but for the consumer to be fully informed a proper designation of the food should be given and we so *recommend*. This places no obstacle in the way of an additional statement of purpose.

48. *Negative statements.* These are sometimes put forward as appropriate designations, such as 'meatless sausage' or 'non-dairy creamer'. Here again the statement is inadequate to inform the consumer of the 'true nature' of the food and should be accompanied by a description adequate to qualify as an *appropriate designation.* We *recommend* accordingly.

49. *The process undergone by a food.* Particulars of the physical condition of the food eg 'dried' or the specific treatment undergone eg 'pasteurised' are required to be specified as part of the name of the food by the EEC Food Labelling Directive, but only where omission of such information 'could create confusion in the mind of the purchaser'. We consider that the existing definition of 'appropriate designation' has, in general, a similar effect and as such a further general provision is not required. With particular foods there may however be a need to require a declaration of the process or physical condition where this has modified the properties of the food. Such declarations are best dealt with on a commodity basis (and not generally) where all the particular circumstances can be assessed in detail. We have made recommendations in paragraphs 126-127 below dealing with foods which have undergone one particular process, drying.

The appropriate designation requirement (Regulations 5(1) and 5(2))

50. Prepacked food as defined in paragraph 33 (other than intoxicating liquor, see paragraph 136 *et seq*) must, by virtue of Regulations 5(1) and 5(2), carry certain information on the label. Regulation 5(2)(a) requires that labels of foods consisting of a single ingredient bear an appropriate designation as defined in paragraph 40 whilst Regulation 5(2)(b)(i) requires that the labels of foods with two or more ingredients carry an appropriate designation or common or usual name as discussed in paragraph 42. This important requirement, the cornerstone of the Regulations, requiring as it does that *all* foods which are prepacked (other than some prepacked and sold by the retailer — see paragraph 77) are identified by a specific description in one form or another, is the basic means of providing the consumer with information enabling a fair and informed choice to be made between the many foods offered for sale. We *recommend* therefore that this basic requirement continues as part of the law. A similar requirement in the EEC Food Labelling Directive also recognises this basic right of the consumer to be informed about food offered for sale.

Percentage declaration of the main ingredient

51. Article 7 of the EEC Food Labelling Directive requires that where the labelling of a food 'places emphasis on the presence or low content of one or more ingredients which are essential to the specific properties of the foodstuff, or where the description of the foodstuff has the same effect . . . . . .' the minimum or maximum percentage, as appropriate, of the ingredient used in the manufacture of the food must be declared. The declaration would be given either next to the appropriate designation or in the ingredients list. This requirement does not apply to labelling 'which is intended to characterise' the food as part of the name or which is required by Community or national provisions applicable to certain foods. Ingredients used only in small quantities such as flavourings are also exempt.

52. The wording of this requirement is in our view peculiarly vague. It is not clear, for instance, whether nutritional claims such as 'contains vitamin C' will be covered by the provision. If they are, there would appear to be some overlap with the requirements of the EEC Directive on Foods for Particular Nutritional Uses (discussed in our Second Report on Claims and Misleading Descriptions). The wording of the requirement may also prove troublesome to incorporate into UK legislation and then may prove difficult to enforce. The concept of declaring the percentage of the main or characterising ingredient, such as fruit in jam is acceptable and accords with our views (paragraph 17). We consider that there are many foods for which percentage declaration should be encouraged as providing the consumer with useful information which can readily be understood and which may prove useful as a means of comparison between different types of the same product. Obviously such a provision cannot easily have its scope and application made clear in general legislation which also has application to many foods, where it would be difficult to gauge either the main or the characterising ingredient, without

20

specific rules. We would prefer to see the requirement for percentage declaration left to individual commodity regulations or to EEC commodity directives. The provision in the EEC Food Labelling Directive is an inadequate method of formulating a valuable concept which could in the future be a central indicator to consumers in their selection of some classes of foods.

53. We have been told that a declaration of the minimum or maximum percentage of an ingredient is meant to apply where emphasis on labels either in pictures or in statements goes beyond the information necessary to meet the requirements of the law concerning the presence of that ingredient. We consider that even with this clarification the provision will be difficult to enforce. If undue or misleading emphasis is given on a label, then it may be that an offence is committed under Section 6 of the Food and Drugs Act 1955. However, a degree of emphasis may be given to a particular ingredient which is not in itself misleading but this could still fall within the terms of the Directive's provisions. Thus the examples 'made with finest butter' and 'contains real fruit' would seem to us to be candidates for percentage declarations. Although we can envisage occasions when such information may be useful, we can envisage many more when manufacturers will face great problems in deciding when a declaration should be made and equally enforcement officers in deciding whether they agree with manufacturers' judgements.

54. We remain convinced that a percentage declaration is more appropriate to legislation controlling specific foods where the need and the problems can be carefully assessed. We have therefore kept and will keep the possibility of such a provision very much in mind in our reviews of individual commodities. We hope nevertheless that the provision in the EEC Food Labelling Directive can be written into UK legislation in as clear a way as possible to retain the useful functions of a percentage declaration and to reduce any problems to a minimum. We foresee a need for great co-operation between manufacturers and enforcement authorities until all concerned become familiar with this new provision.

Ingredient listing (Regulations 5(1), 5(2), 5(4), 5(5) and 5(6))

55. Food which consists of two or more ingredients and which is prepacked as defined in paragraph 33 must carry a declaration of those ingredients on the label. Regulations 5(1) and 5(2)(b)(ii) require that an appropriate designation of each ingredient must be given in the form of a list. Some foods do not have to carry a list of ingredients on the label: exemptions from ingredient listing are discussed in paragraphs 70-82 below.

56. *Definition of ingredient.* There is no definition of 'ingredient' in the 1970 Regulations but we have already recommended in paragraph 10 of our Report on Ingredient Listing that a definition along the lines of that in the EEC Food Labelling Directive should be included in future legislation. It has been suggested in representations on that Report that this definition should

recognise that certain additives need not be declared if they are present in only very small amounts and have no effect on the food. We deal with this in paragraphs 63 and 64 below.

57.   *Declaration of water.* The presence of water as an ingredient of food does not have to be declared (proviso (a) to Regulation 5(2)(b)(ii)). The inclusion of water within the definition of 'ingredient' as recommended in our Report on Ingredient Listing will mean that added water will in future need to be declared as an ingredient. We have however made separate recommendations about the declaration of added water in our 1978 Report on Water in Food. Such a declaration will also be required under the provisions of the EEC Food Labelling Directive and the EEC requirement is also discussed in our Report on Water in Food.

58.   *The appropriate designation of the ingredient.* As indicated in paragraph 41, the definition of 'appropriate designation' in Regulation 3(1) requires that each ingredient be listed by a specific name or description. Each ingredient referred to in a list must therefore be described as specifically as possible and there is no opportunity to use a generic term other than one of those listed in the Regulations and discussed in paragraph 59. If the ingredients list is to be of use to the purchaser, it must be as informative and as accurate as possible and the number of generic terms used must be kept to the minimum consistent with this need for clear and positive information. We *recommend* accordingly.

59.   *Generic terms for ingredients.* Certain ingredients are not required to be listed by their specific name but may instead be described by one of the generic terms listed in paragraphs 1-3 of Schedule 2 (Regulation 6(1) refers). We have already fully discussed this provision in our Report on Ingredient Listing (at Appendix 2) and a revised list of generic terms, consistent with our general principle at paragraph 58, has been recommended. Paragraph 47 of that Report details our views on the use of these terms.

60.   *Constituents of ingredients.* Proviso (b) to Regulation 5(2)(b)(ii) requires that where an ingredient is made up of two or more constituents, an appropriate designation of each of these constituents must be listed in the appropriate places in the ingredients list. Regulation 5(6) however allows such an ingredient to be listed by its appropriate designation provided the appropriate designations of the constituents follow immediately or are in close proximity. If an ingredient or constituent contains a permitted preservative, antioxidant, colouring matter, emulsifier, stabiliser, artificial sweetener, bleaching agent, improving agent, or solvent or any flavouring and the amount of each such substance present in the food is insufficient to produce a preservative, antioxidant, etc effect, the appropriate designation may take the form 'X with permitted preservative' etc. Similarly, if an ingredient or constituent contains any mineral hydrocarbon and the amount present is insufficient to produce a significant effect on the food, the appropriate designation may also be in the form 'X with mineral hydrocarbon'. Proviso (a) to Regulation 5(6) allows the word 'permitted' to be omitted from these

descriptions and proviso (b) allows an appropriate designation to be given in place of the generic terms 'preservative', 'antioxidant', etc. Some foods are exempt from the need to declare their constituents when forming an ingredient of another food (Regulation 6(1)). These foods are listed in Part III of Schedule 2 to the 1970 Labelling of Food Regulations. We have discussed these fully in paragraphs 59 to 61 of our Report on Ingredient Listing.

61.   The existing provisions in the 1970 Regulations governing the declaration of constituents of ingredients are useful to consumers, allowing recognition of the fact that certain foods used as ingredients will themselves be made of other components which can be found in the ingredients list. Regulation 5(6), which allows the constituents to be listed alongside the appropriate designation of the ingredient, permits this to be seen very clearly. If however the constituents of an ingredient are listed separately amongst the ingredients (as permitted by proviso (b) to Regulation 5(2)(b)(ii)) the composition of the food will not be so clearly apparent and as such the ingredient list will be less informative. We therefore *recommend* that where an ingredient is made up of two or more constituents, the appropriate designations of those constituents should always appear in immediate proximity to the appropriate designation of the ingredient. This recommendation supports our view expressed in paragraph 54 (k) of our Report on Ingredient Listing that, for instance, with pie products it would be more helpful to the consumer if the pastry constituents were listed separately from the filling.

62.   The other provisions allowing constituents to be declared as 'X with permitted preservative' etc are also helpful to the purchaser. With constituents present in very small amounts, declaration in this way will give an indication of just how small these amounts are yet at the same time will indicate that these are part of an ingredient rather than having been added separately to the food. We *recommend* that these provisions be continued in future legislation.

63.   *'Carry-over' of additives.* The 'carry-over' of certain additives into a food through their use in an ingredient or as a processing aid is dealt with in proviso (c) to Regulation 5(6). Where any permitted preservative or permitted antioxidant is present in an ingredient in a quantity insufficient to produce a preservative or antioxidant effect on the *ingredient* or in a proportion of less than 5% (calculated on the weight of the ingredient) of the amount permitted in that ingredient by the Preservatives in Food Regulations 1975 or the Antioxidant in Food Regulations 1978, the presence of that preservative or antioxidant need not be stated in the ingredients lists.

64.   The point below which ingredients present in very small amounts need not be declared is difficult to determine. Even if the principle is accepted, any figure chosen must inevitably be arbitrary. We discussed this problem in paragraphs 95 to 99 of our 1964 Report on Food Labelling and we took the view that additives such as preservatives, antioxidants or mineral oils need not be declared when present in an ingredient in very small amounts. We consequently recommended a 5% cut-off point based on the maximum

amount of preservative, antioxidant or mineral oil permitted in the ingredient. (Our recommendation relating to mineral oil was not subsequently implemented.) We remain of the view that provisions are necessary along existing lines to deal with the presence of very small amounts of additives and we so *recommend*. We consider, however, that to be consistent the principle should be recognised for all additives and the effects of the additive should be related to the food rather than the ingredient and we *recommend* accordingly. The provisions of Article 6.4(c)(ii) of the EEC Food Labelling Directive are not inconsistent with our views. The Article states that the following additives are not regarded as ingredients:

'— whose presence in a given foodstuff is solely due to the fact that they were contained in one or more ingredients of that foodstuff, provided that they serve no technological function in the finished product,

— which are used as processing aids'.

When this provision is implemented, the 5% cut-off in the 1970 Regulations which at present applies to permitted preservatives and permitted antioxidants and which acts as a valuable safeguard will no longer be available. The removal of this upper limit for the amounts of additives which may be present but which do not have to be declared might lead to problems with the inclusion of larger amounts of undeclared additives, but we are satisfied that the wording of the provision in the EEC Food Labelling Directive should be sufficient to prevent abuses. If problems do occur, the imposition of an upper limit may need to be examined.

65. *Order of ingredient listing.* Regulation 5(4) allows a choice when listing ingredients or constituents: if the quantity or proportion of each ingredient is not specified they must be listed in descending order by weight as used in the manufacturing process. The vast majority of ingredients lists follow this latter method of declaration. Although very few manufacturers choose to specify the quantity of each ingredient or constituent and although we would not wish to advocate extension of this practice we *recommend* that this alternative method should continue to be available. This method is increasingly employed in some other countries, including within the EEC. However, the provisions of Article 6.5(a) of the EEC Food Labelling Directive would appear still to require the listing of ingredients to be in descending order by weight even if the amounts are specified.

66. *Dried ingredients.* An ingredient or constituent which is used in a food in a dried, dehydrated or concentrated state may be placed in the ingredients list as though it had first been reconstituted (Regulation 5(4)(a)). Foods which are sold dried, dehydrated or concentrated for reconstitution before consumption may bear a declaration of ingredients listed in the order these ingredients will take following reconstitution (Regulation 5(4)(b)). Both these provisions recognise that the order of dried ingredients may change after reconstitution, some ingredients taking up more water than others, and ingredient lists are therefore allowed to take this into account. We *recommend* that these provisions be maintained. There may be a need in certain circumstances to

provide an assigned hydration value in legislation for particular foods such as soya isolates to facilitate listing ingredients in this way. We discuss a provision for vegetable protein products when used in meat products in our forthcoming Report on Meat Products. We also *recommend* that where an ingredient is placed in the ingredients list as though it had first been reconstituted, the appropriate designation should be qualified by a description such as 'when reconstituted' to make clear that this has taken place. Article 6.5(a) of the EEC Food Labelling Directive contains provisions similar to those of Regulation 5(4)(a) and (b).

67. *Alphabetical listing of ingredients.* Where a food consists solely of, or contains, mixed fruit or mixed vegetables and where no particular fruit or vegetable 'significantly predominates' in proportion by weight, those ingredients may be listed in alphabetical order. Where these are listed with other ingredients it must be done in such a way as not to mislead as to the quantities used in the manufacture of the food (Regulation 5(4)(c) refers). We *recommend* that this provision continue in legislation. A similar provision is contained in Article 6.5(a) of the EEC Food Labelling Directive. We have been told that this provision should also apply to foods consisting solely of, or containing, nuts since these are included in the Customs Tariff with 'fruit'. We consider that a food consisting of, for example, mixed nuts should be allowed to make use of the provision and we therefore *recommend* that, for the purposes of the alphabetical listing of ingredients, nuts should be included.

68. *Heading to ingredients lists.* Regulation 5(5) at present requires that ingredients lists be headed 'Ingredients' or 'Ingredients in order of quantity'. Where the dried or dehydrated foods referred to in paragraph 66 above carry a list of ingredients in reconstituted order, the list must be headed 'Ingredients in order, by weight, when reconstituted' or 'Ingredients when reconstituted'. Foods consisting solely of mixed fruit or mixed vegetables (paragraph 67 above) must carry an ingredients list headed 'Ingredients in alphabetical order'. Similar provisions are contained in Article 6.5(a) of the EEC Food Labelling Directive for mixed fruit, vegetables, spices or herbs, for which the list must be accompanied by an expression such as 'in variable proportion'.

69. We have already recommended in paragraph 58 of our Report on Ingredient Listing that ingredient lists should be headed 'Ingredients Used'. We recommended this phrase because it conveyed the idea that the ingredients listed were those used in the 'mixing bowl' even though they might have changed during the manufacturing process. In reconsidering this recommendation in the light of our general recommendations in this Report, we reached the view that to be of most use to the purchaser, the heading to the ingredients list should *also* make clear that the ingredients were listed in order of quantity. To achieve both these purposes without ambiguity, the list would need to be headed 'Ingredients used in order of quantity' or a similar phrase. This reflects both aspects of ingredient listing referred to above. We do not however regard such a labelling requirement as a practicable measure because of the length of the phrase. Since the heading cannot readily incorporate both

25

aspects using fewer words, we decided that it should reflect whichever was of greater use to the purchaser. On balance, we decided that an indication that the ingredients were listed in quantity order would be of greater use than an indication that the ingredients were as added in the 'mixing bowl'. We therefore *recommend* that in future ingredients lists be headed 'Ingredients in weight order'. Ingredients would still of course continue to be *listed* as used in the 'mixing bowl'. The other headings referred to in paragraph 68 should be appropriately changed and we *recommend* accordingly. Where the quantities or proportions of ingredients are listed (if permitted by the EEC Food Labelling Directive), the heading should be 'Ingredients used'. These recommendations supersede recommendation 23 in our 1977 Report on Beer and recommendation 9 in our Report on Ingredient Listing.

Exemptions from ingredient listing (Regulations 5(1), 6, 7 and Schedules 2 and 5)

70. Our Report on Ingredient Listing at Appendix 2 sets out our recommendations about those foods exempt from the need to list ingredients by virtue of Regulations 5(1) and 6(1). That Report also deals with those foods similarly exempt by virtue of Regulations 4(3), (4) and (5) and Regulation 16. We reiterate our view that all prepacked foods apart from single ingredient foods and the two special cases referred to in paragraphs 41 and 42 of our Report on Ingredient Listing should in future be required to bear a list of ingredients. This view is supported by the general principles of food labelling we have established in paragraph 27 above.

71. *Exempt foods required to list certain additives.* In paragraph 3 of our Report on Ingredient Listing we noted that some foods, although at present exempt from the need to carry a list of ingredients, were required to declare certain additives on the label. Regulation 7(4) of the 1970 Regulations requires that those foods exempt from an ingredient declaration by virtue of Regulation 6(1) and Part I of Schedule 2 must carry a declaration of any permitted preservative, antioxidant, colouring matter or artificial sweetener present, none of these being naturally present in the food. Regulation 7(1) requires that the declaration takes the form:

> 'contains permitted preservative
> permitted antioxidant
> permitted colour
> saccharin'.

The word 'permitted' may be omitted (proviso (a) to Regulation 7 (1)) and an appropriate designation of the additive may be substituted for any of the generic terms (proviso (b)). Artificial sweetening tablets, although exempt from ingredient declaration, do not have to carry the statement 'contains saccharin' (proviso (c)) since 'saccharin' must be referred to in the appropriate designation by virtue of the requirements of the Artificial Sweeteners in Food Regulations 1969[22].

---

[22]England and Wales SI 1969 No. 1818
Scotland SI 1969 No. 1848 (S16)
Northern Ireland SR & O (NI) 1969 No. 346

72. Proviso (d) to Regulation 7(1) exempts from declaration permitted preservatives or antioxidants present in an ingredient in only very small amounts. This is similar to the provision discussed in paragraphs 63 and 64. Where permitted preservatives or antioxidants are present in a food only by virtue of their presence in an ingredient and in a quantity insufficient to produce a preservative or antioxidant effect *on the food* and in a proportion of less than 5% by weight of the amount permitted in that ingredient, or in a quantity insufficient to produce a preservative or antioxidant effect *on the ingredient,* the presence of those additives need not be declared. Regulation 7(2) permits a declaration of the quantity by weight of the additive present in the statement 'contains permitted preservative' etc and Regulation 7(3) exempts from any statement of additives present containers whose greatest dimension is not more than 5 cm and for which, because of lack of space, the inclusion of such a statement is impracticable. A minimum size of type for the declaration required by Regulation 7 is prescribed in paragraph 8 of Schedule 5.

73. Our recommendations for the declaration of the ingredients of nearly all prepacked food would render Regulation 7 unnecessary in the future. However, it appears likely that when the EEC Food Labelling Directive is implemented in the United Kingdom, some exemptions from ingredients listing, such as that for alcoholic beverages, will continue to be permitted. In these circumstances, we *recommend* that Regulation 7 be retained until such time as full ingredient listing is required for all foods. Although we consider that the present 5% cut-off acts as a valuable safeguard, we accept that proviso (d) to Regulation 7(1) should be brought into line with our recommendations in paragraph 64 relating to 'carry-over' of additives.

74. *Exemption for small containers.* We have already recommended against an exemption from ingredient declaration for small containers (Regulation 6(4)) in our Report on Ingredient Listing; our views are set out in paragraph 46 of that Report at Appendix 2.

75. *Ingredient listing for exempt foods.* Regulation 6(6) requires that if a food which is exempt from ingredient declaration carries on the label a reference to any of its ingredients, and that reference is not part of the appropriate designation or common or usual name or a brand or trade name or part of a statement required by regulations, then a full list of ingredients must be given. The need for this Regulation will disappear once all foods carry a list of ingredients on the label but, in the event of any foods remaining exempt under legislation to implement the EEC Food Labelling Directive, consideration should be given to the retention of this provision. We *recommend* accordingly.

76. *Exemption for the producer/retailer.* In paragraphs 27, 28 and 32 of our Report on Ingredient Listing we referred to some of the problems of ingredient listing faced by the small master baker and the smaller manufacturer of ice-cream. Although we recognised the principle of across-the-board ingredient

listing whatever the size of business concerned, we said in paragraph 28 of that Report that we would be examining the problems faced by small businesses in a later report. We have consequently examined this subject in some detail and our findings are set out in paragraphs 77-82 below.

77.   A measure of recognition of the difficulties facing the producer/retailer is already afforded by Regulations 6(2) and 6(3) of the 1970 Labelling of Food Regulations. A food consisting of *one ingredient* prepacked by a retailer and sold on the premises where it was prepacked or sold from his delivery van is exempt from the requirement to bear an appropriate designation (Regulation 6(2)). This exemption does not however apply if the label or container of the food bears any words referring in any way to the food 'other than such as are necessary to indicate the price and quantity'. Regulation 6(3)(a) similarly exempts from the name and address requirement (Regulation 5(3)) *any* food prepacked by a retailer and sold by him on the premises where it was prepacked or sold from his delivery van. Regulation 6(3)(b) exempts from the same requirement flour confectionery or bread sold by the producer provided the producer's name is displayed on the premises where the food is sold. A further measure of recognition is afforded by the exclusion of flour confectionery, bread and sandwiches (foods commonly sold by producer/retailers) from the definition of 'prepacked' when sold in wholly transparent containers (as discussed in paragraphs 33 and 36).

78.   There are thus at present a range of exemptions from particular labelling requirements which are available to the producer/retailer to help deal with some of the practical difficulties of labelling food on the retail premises. Additionally, a proportion of the food that he sells, such as flour confectionery, is currently exempt from an ingredient declaration even when prepacked as defined and if he also sells any unwrapped foods, much of this too is exempt from any labelling requirement. The degree of labelling required to be carried out by the producer/retailer may therefore not need to be extensive and might well be negligible where much non-prepacked food is sold. Our recommendations for full ingredient listing and the possible effects of the EEC Food Labelling Directive discussed in paragraph 36 are however likely to change the present requirements significantly in that foods such as flour confectionery and bread would in future be required to bear an ingredient declaration when prepacked. If all producer/retailers were required by law to label a much greater proportion of the food they sell with lists of ingredients, this could present difficulties, particularly for the smaller business. With the small master baker, for instance, variations in the supply and composition of bought-in ingredients would result in frequent changes in ingredients lists. Variations in the ingredients used due to changes in recipes, the use of 'left-over' ingredients (eg dough remaining from one product being mixed with dough from another, the doughs being of different composition), and estimating rather than measuring quantities of ingredients, would all make accurate listing difficult. Where small quantities of a food such as cheese or meat products derived from bulk packs are prepacked by the retailer,

ingredient information is often not available. There would also be the cost of labels and labour.

79.   The difficulties involved when prepacking from bulk, such as wrapping small portions of cheese, can be fairly easily overcome by a requirement that ingredient information should be provided throughout the distribution chain. Our recommendation in paragraph 87 should deal adequately with this. The other difficulties referred to in paragraph 78 are not so easy to resolve: total exemption from ingredient declaration would seem to be the only way to avoid the costs of labour and changing of labels. With this in mind we obtained information about prepacking by retailers in one particular county and the retailers' views on ingredient listing. The information showed that the foods most commonly prepacked were cheese, meat, and fresh fruit and vegetables. The majority of shops packing in this way (other than bakers) only did so for one or two foods. Of the retailers asked for their reactions to the possibility of more stringent labelling requirements, roughly half said, not unnaturally, that they would cease prepacking. Many foods are wrapped for hygiene purposes or to prevent confectionery drying out too quickly and it would seem to be a retrograde step if this practice were to cease as a result of the introduction of new labelling requirements.

80.   In the circumstances, after very full consideration, we have concluded that there is a case for the exemption from ingredient listing of food prepacked by the producer/retailer. Any such exemption poses problems however in that if it is set simply in terms of exempting food prepacked and sold on the same premises, it would cover many of the larger supermarkets which prepare and wrap a number of fresh foods such as cheese on the store premises. We do not however consider that there is any satisfactory or equitable way in which an exemption will apply only to those premises presented with particular difficulties such as the small baker who bakes and sells his produce on the same premises. The exemption will therefore need to apply to any appropriate retail premises irrespective of size and we consider that the best form of exemption would be one along the lines of that already available under Regulations 6(2) and (3) of the 1970 Labelling of Food Regulations referred to in paragraph 77 above. We therefore *recommend* that food prepacked by a retailer and sold by him on the premises where it was prepacked or from a delivery van owned by him should be exempt from an ingredient declaration. This exemption should however be restricted to food sold from a single premises: this will have the effect of limiting the exemption to individual premises and will exclude sales from two or more premises trading under the same name and receiving supplies from a single source. These latter operations will usually include the larger shops and supermarket chains. We do not consider that organisations of this size would be faced with the same practical labelling difficulties as are encountered especially by small retailers operating in single premises and as such a similar exemption could not be justified. To help bakers who might have a separate bake-house next to the shop, 'premises' should be defined as 'all buildings at one address'. As a further help, flour confectionery in crimp cases should not be regarded as 'prepacked' as

discussed in paragraph 31. We appreciate that our recommended exemption may also cover some supermarkets which do their own prepacking and we *recommend* that further consideration be given to this point in the light of representations received when drafting future legislation.

81. Article 12 of the EEC Food Labelling Directive allows Member States to adopt detailed rules in relation to food 'packaged on the sales premises at the consumer's request or prepackaged for direct sale' and Member States may require less information for these than for other foods provided that it is sufficient for the consumer. Our recommendations in paragraph 80 to meet the problems of the producer/retailer should be acceptable under this Article. We have noted in paragraph 36 that food packed in wholly transparent containers will probably be regarded as prepacked under the terms of the Directive. Whatever the effect this might have in relation to food sold by retail, when such food is sold by the producer/retailer as defined in paragraph 80, we *recommend* that it be treated as non-prepacked and that the price, quantity and the retailer's name and address may appear on the wrapper without the exemption being lost.

82. Having recommended the concessions in paragraphs 80 and 81 we further *recommend* that the producer/retailer should no longer be exempt from labelling the food he sells with an appropriate designation. We consider that an appropriate designation is of greater importance to purchasers than the ingredients list and it should always be given so as to inform the consumer. This recommendation would mean that all food sold by such retailers, prepacked as defined in the legislation, will have to be identified at the time of sale. This may be by ticket or notice rather than by a label attached to the individual foods. We discuss a similar requirement for all non-prepacked foods in paragraphs 89-95 below.

The name and address requirement (Regulations 5(1) and 5(3))

83. Regulation 5(3), by virtue of Regulation 5(1), requires that labels of prepacked food carry the name and business address of either the packer or the labeller. Where the food is packed or labelled on behalf of, or on the instructions of, another person who carries on business at a UK address, the name and address of that other person may be given on the label instead of that of the packer or labeller (proviso (a)). Regulation 5(3) does not apply to any bottle containing intoxicating liquor which was bottled before 1 January 1970 and the label of which complies with any appropriate legislation in force on 1 January 1970 (proviso (b)). This latter provision is included to take account of vintage wines etc, which when bottled were labelled in accordance with the Labelling of Food Order 1953 which allowed a registered trade mark in place of the name and address. But for proviso (b), any such wines falling to be controlled by the 1970 Labelling of Food Regulations, if sold now, would contravene Regulation 5(3).

84. We consider that Regulation 5(3) and proviso (a) are working

satisfactorily and we *recommend* their retention in law. There is a similar provision in Article 3.1(6) of the EEC Food Labelling Directive. Proviso (b) will however need to be examined to establish how much intoxicating liquor labelled in accordance with the Labelling of Food Order 1953, and likely to be controlled by future labelling legislation, remains to be sold when that legislation comes into force. We *recommend* accordingly.

85.   As referred to in paragraph 77, Regulation 6(3)(a) exempts from the name and address requirement food prepacked by a retailer and Regulation 6(3)(b) similarly exempts bread and flour confectionery sold by the producer. We consider that both provisions are working satisfactorily and we *recommend* that they be retained.

86.   Regulation 6(5) permits the omission of the name and address from the labels of foods exempt from an ingredient declaration if the greatest dimension of the container is not more than 5 cm and there is insufficient space on the label. This Regulation will of course no longer be appropriate once practically all foods are required to list ingredients. Even if some exemptions remain as a result of implementation of the EEC Food Labelling Directive, we do not consider Regulation 6(5) should remain and we *recommend* accordingly. As we said in paragraph 46 of our Report on Ingredient Listing, we are not generally in favour of any exemption for small containers, especially where, as in this instance, there is no minimum size of type requirement for the information.

Sales other than by retail (Regulation 8)

87.   Regulation 8 requires that when prepacked food is delivered pursuant to a sale other than a retail sale it must be labelled in accordance with the Regulations or, if delivered unlabelled, the purchaser must be provided within fourteen days with an invoice or other document containing information which will enable a retailer to comply with the Regulations. Article 11.1(b) of the EEC Food Labelling Directive provides that Member States may authorise that all or some of the required labelling particulars 'be given only on the relevant trade documents when the foodstuffs are prepackaged and marketed prior to their sale to the ultimate consumer'. We were told that enforcement authorities have experienced difficulties with the enforcement of Regulation 8 in that food delivered in this way to a retailer is usually sold to a consumer within the fourteen day period and the invoice or other document required is seldom produced. Sales other than by retail include the sale of bulk packs to retailers and catering packs to caterers, many of which can nowadays be found on retail sale, especially in 'cash and carry' stores. In these circumstances it is right that all such packs should be labelled with the same information as normal retail packs. Where catering packs or bulk packs are sold to the general public they are of course retail sales as defined in the Regulations since they are sales to a person buying otherwise than for the purpose of re-sale. It is our view that information about food should be available throughout the distribution chain to enable it to be labelled correctly when sold to the public.

We think it is particularly important that when food is sold prepacked in a container to a caterer who may wish merely to break bulk before selling to the consumer or, alternatively, when sold to a cash-and-carry store which may not touch the packaging in any way before allowing the food to be sold to the consumer, it should be labelled in accordance with the labelling requirements for retail sales and we so *recommend*. In respect of sales to a caterer, our recommendations in paragraphs 34 and 35 should be adequate for this purpose but the recommendation above would extend the same control to sales to cash-and-carry stores.

88.   We do not believe that all the normally required information need or should appear on containers of food which are moving from one manufacturer to another, particularly as such containers could include bulk containers. We therefore *recommend* that where food is sold to a manufacturer for the purpose of his business the necessary information, if not appearing on the container, must be made available to the purchaser within fourteen days. We believe that the tighter provision we have recommended relating to caterers will solve the major problems of enforcement officers and think it unnecessary to burden manufacturers with a requirement to give similar information on labels for foods in transit during the manufacturing process. It must be remembered that with more foods being required to carry a full list of ingredients manufacturers will have to supply details of the ingredients of the foods they produce to other manufacturers using these foods in recipes. A statutory provision is therefore even less needed than if the legislative requirements were to remain as at present. It is also important to note that these recommendations relate to large packs of foods and not to outer cases of prepacked food. In the latter instances, the small prepacks will carry all the necessary information and we would not necessarily expect the outer pack to bear more than the name of the product or an indication of this for the purposes of identification and, with the introduction of statutory date marking, some indication of the life of the product.

Non-prepacked foods (Regulation 9 and Schedules 3 and 5)

89.   The requirements for the provision of information about non-prepacked foods are at present far less onerous than those for prepacked food. Regulation 9(1) requires that those foods referred to in Part I of Schedule 3, ie all non-prepacked foods containing two or more ingredients, other than bread, flour confectionery, sugar confectionery, chocolate confectionery or any drink or wholly liquid product must when sold by retail (including when it is exposed for sale) be accompanied by a ticket on or in immediate proximity to the food giving the appropriate designation or common or usual name: fish must also be labelled by means of a ticket with the name laid down in Schedule 1 to the Regulations or, if not listed in the Schedule, an appropriate designation or common or usual name. Sandwiches and foods with one main ingredient, packed in wholly transparent containers (see paragraphs 33 and 36), are regarded as non-prepacked under the Regulations and will similarly need to be ticketed with the appropriate designation or common or usual name.

Paragraph 9 of Schedule 5 requires that the height of the letters in any statement required by Regulation 9(1) must not be such as is likely to mislead as to the nature, substance, or quality of the food and the height of the letters in a word describing a minor ingredient must not give undue prominence to that ingredient when the statement is taken as a whole. If any of these foods is sold for immediate consumption at or near the place of sale, or is sold without having been previously exposed for sale, it is sufficient for the purchaser to be notified of the particulars at or before delivery of the food (Regulations 9(3) and (4)).

90. Regulation 9(2) further requires that where non-prepacked foods consisting of two or more ingredients, other than those foods listed in Part II of Schedule 3, contain permitted preservative, antioxidant, colouring matter or artificial sweetener (none of which being naturally present), the presence of these additives must be declared on a ticket as in Regulations 7(1) and (2) (see paragraph 71 above). Food sold for immediate consumption at or near the place of sale does not have to comply with this requirement (Regulation 9(3)(b)). The statement on the ticket must take the form 'contains preservative' etc. The 1976 Labelling of Food (Amendment) Regulations allow that if these additives are present in the food only because of their use in an ingredient and that ingredient is exempt from a declaration of its constitutents when part of a prepacked food (as listed in Part III of Schedule 2), their presence does not have to be declared.

91. The existing requirements for the ticketing of non-prepacked foods are therefore not only complicated but inconsistent and confusing. The retailer will find the requirements difficult to understand and we have been told that retailers not surprisingly, often find it hard to appreciate the more subtle and detailed aspects of such legislation as applies here. The requirement to declare additives is also difficult to comply with because there is no parallel requirement for the requisite compositional information to be passed down through the distribution chain when food is non-prepacked. (We have already discussed a similar requirement for the provision of labelling information in paragraph 87.) There is a clear need in these circumstances for a basic and simple requirement which will apply to all non-prepacked food and which will be more susceptible to understanding and consequent compliance than the existing provisions.

92. We discussed the labelling of non-prepacked food sold by retail in paragraphs 79-83 of our 1964 Report on Food Labelling. At that time it was not considered necessary to apply labelling provisions to all unwrapped food but there were two kinds of such foods for which we considered that labelling provisions were necessary: these were compound foods, where consumers might be in doubt as to what they were being offered, and fresh foods, where the type or variety was important to the consumer. We consequently recommended in paragraph 81 of our 1964 Report that when sold non-prepacked, all compound food (except bread, flour confectionery, sugar confectionery and chocolate confectionery) should indicate the common or

usual name or appropriate designation on a ticket. Fish, cheese, apples, pears, plums and potatoes should be ticketed with the variety, sausages with the type of meat, meat and edible offal with the type of meat or edible offal and, where appropriate, the joint or cut of meat. Meat and fish pies should be ticketed with the appropriate designation. Confectionery was excluded from any requirement because we considered at that time that to require tickets for a display of cakes, for example, with varied appropriate designations would be onerous to retailers and of little benefit to consumers. The foods listed as requiring identification were considered the most important ones where consumers were liable to be confused and where a display ticket indicating variety could prevent the customer being orally misled. The need to differentiate between fresh and thawed-out frozen fish was examined in paragraph 83 of our 1964 Report but it was not thought that there should be any statutory requirement since it would be impossible to enforce and might be taken to imply that quick-frozen fish was inferior to fresh fish (which may have been stored with ice or even without cooling).

93. In paragraph 93 of our 1964 Report on Food Labelling it was recommended that non-prepacked foods should carry a special declaration of additives parallel to that recommended for foods in general. The additives to be declared were those whose function it was to ensure that a food was presented in a sound and attractive condition but which might give a misleading impression as to its nature or quality: preservatives, antioxidants, colours, artificial sweeteners, bleachers, improvers and flavourings were regarded as such although no declaration of flavourings was eventually recommended. This group of additives was regarded as so important that, apart from flavourings, a special separate declaration was recommended to be required on the labels of prepacked food, even if a list of ingredients was already present. The requirements in the existing Regulation 9 of the 1970 Labelling Regulations reflect only partially the recommendations in our 1964 Report.

94. We have subsequently examined in detail the sale of non-prepacked foods under present-day conditions. Sales of foods which are traditionally non-prepacked, such as bread and flour confectionery sold by the small baker, sausages and meat pies, would seem to be continuing at a steady rate but sales of other non-prepacked foods seem to have increased with the growth in the numbers of 'take-away' establishments and restaurants: sales of food from licensed premises have also increased, whether these are sandwiches, snacks or complete meals. We have already dealt with sales of draught beer in our 1977 Report on Beer. In the light of increasing consumer awareness about food and the increase in the demand for greater information, the sale of non-prepacked food cannot be ignored. A consumer has as much right to know what he is buying when a customer in a restaurant or 'take-away' as when he selects prepacked food from a supermarket shelf. The general law already protects against misdescription but there is no positive general requirement for non-prepacked food to be precisely identified. This is particularly important with unprocessed foods such as meat, poultry, fish, and fresh fruit and vegetables.

Non-prepacked fish must already be identified however it is sold and we would wish to see this principle extended to all other non-prepacked foods. We therefore *recommend* as a general principle that all non-prepacked food when sold by retail should be identified by its *appropriate designation* (as defined in paragraph 42) by means of a ticket or any other suitable method of identification such as on a menu, a price list or other document clearly displayed in the shop or in a catering establishment. In these circumstances the consumer will have a right to know and will be given a precise indication of what is being offered for sale and the retailer will know that he must identify all his goods. This requirement should prove easy to understand and to comply with and there should be far less difficulty in enforcement. Protection against oral 'passing-off' will also be greatly increased.

95.   Non-prepacked butchers' meat and offal and non-prepacked fresh fruit and vegetables, because of their importance to the consumer, merit additional requirements. These requirements are however equally relevant to the sale of these foods when prepacked and we have accordingly made appropriate recommendations in Section IV of this Report dealing with specific labelling requirements for particular foods (paragraphs 109-120).

96.   *Declarations of additives.* As referred to in paragraph 90, certain non-prepacked foods must declare certain classes of additive by means of a ticket close to the food. The foods listed in Part II of Schedule 3 to the 1970 Labelling of Food Regulations are however exempt from such a declaration. Most of these exempt foods are at present also exempt from a declaration of ingredients when prepacked and in these circumstances it would seem appropriate to continue the exemption when non-prepacked. The ending of the exemptions from ingredient listing for prepacked foods means logically that the exemptions for non-prepacked foods should similarly be ended. However, there are two arguments against this: firstly, that we are not convinced that additives should be singled out in this way for declaration in all foods and secondly, that we wish to avoid the possibility of non-prepacked food being festooned with tickets which will detract from the main information being given, confuse the consumer and present the retailer with a major problem in ensuring that all his labels are in the right place. The problems facing a small baker forced to label his bread and cakes with all the additives which have been employed can readily be imagined and we have therefore concluded that there need be no extension of the present requirements of Regulation 9(2). The foods to which Regulation 9(2) at present apply (the most obvious example being meat products) should however continue to be so covered because we believe that the consumer is afforded useful information by this means and the exemptions currently contained in Part II of Schedule 3 should be continued. We *recommend* accordingly. We further *recommend* that the additives listed in Regulation 9(2) continue to be declared. We received representations that mineral hydrocarbons should be similarly declared, especially when present in dried fruit sold loose. We consider this to be a sensible requirement and we *recommend* that mineral hydrocarbons be added to the list of additives to be declared.

35

97. As referred to in paragraph 90, additives which are present in a non-prepacked food only because of their use in an ingredient need not be declared if the ingredient is exempt from a declaration of its constituents when part of a prepacked food. We have been told that this exemption has been abused in some instances where excessive amounts of colouring matter have been added to an ingredient for the deliberate purpose of colouring the food: because of the exemption applying to the ingredient the presence of colour did not have to be declared in the final food. This is clearly not the intention of the provision and we therefore *recommend* that this exemption should apply only where the amount of the additive present in the ingredient does not have any significant effect on the food.

98. *EEC Food Labelling Directive.* Article 12 of the Directive leaves Member States free to adopt detailed rules for foods sold non-prepacked and only certain of the requirements for prepacked food need be applied, provided the consumer receives sufficient information. The UK therefore has freedom of action in this area and our recommendations can form the basis for future legislation without any of the constraints which apply in relation to requirements for prepacked food.

Advertisement of food for sale from vending machines (Regulation 10)

99. Regulation 10 of the 1970 Labelling of Food Regulations requires that the appropriate designation or common or usual name of a food sold from a vending machine should appear in a prominent position on the front of that machine. This does not apply if the required information is conspicuous and legible on or through the outside of the machine. Neither does it apply to any soft drink complying with Regulation 12 of the Soft Drinks Regulations 1964[23] which requires that when a soft drink is sold from a vending machine, the description specified in those Regulations, or a descriptive name of the soft drink, must be clearly visible on or through the outside of the machine and the presence of artificial sweetener must be declared. There are similar requirements in other compositional regulations for products not covered by Part II of the 1970 Labelling of Food Regulations (see paragraphs 239 — 241). All these requirements follow broadly the recommendations in paragraph 168 of our 1964 Report on Food Labelling and they appear to be operating satisfactorily. We therefore *recommend* that they be retained in future legislation.

Use of the word 'flavour' (Regulation 11)

100. *The requirements of Regulation 11.* The present requirements of Regulation 11 of the 1970 Labelling of Food Regulations relating to the use of the word 'flavour' stem from recommendations made in paragraphs 79(i) and

---

[23]England and Wales SI 1965 No 760 as amended by SI 1969 No 1818, SI 1970 No 1597, SI 1972 No 1510, SI 1976 No 295, SI 1977 No 927.
Scotland SI 1964 No 767 (S46) as amended by SI 1969 No 1847 (S163), SI 1970 No 1619 (S131), SI 1972 No 1790 (S141), SI 1976 No 442 (S37).
Northern Ireland SR & O (NI) 1964 No 94 as amended by SR & O (NI) 1969 No 347, SR & O (NI) 1970 No 278, SR & O (NI) 1972 No 318, SR & O (NI) 1976 No 357.

81(iii) of our 1966 Report on Claims and Misleading Descriptions. Regulation 11 requires that if the name of a food is used in an appropriate designation or description or in the name of another food to indicate a specific flavour, such flavour must be derived *wholly or mainly* from the food. (In paragraph 79(i) of our 1966 Report on Claims and Misleading Descriptions we had recommended that the flavour should be *wholly* derived from the food indicated in the name.)If the flavour is not so derived, the word 'flavour' must immediately follow the name of the food in letters of the same size, style and colour. This applies to labels and written advertisements. Advertisements presented orally must include the word 'flavour' spoken audibly and clearly immediately after the name of the food. Pictures of a particular food on labels or in advertisements which suggest that it has imparted a specific flavour may only be used where the flavour is derived *wholly or mainly* from such food. Regulation 11 does not apply to soft drinks eg lemonade labelled in accordance with Regulation 8 of the 1964 Soft Drinks Regulations.

101. The words 'wholly or mainly' are not defined in the Regulations and in our view this could lead to difficulties, particularly where a natural flavour has been boosted with a small amount of artificial flavour (which the words are designed to allow for). It is not possible to define the point at which the flavour is no longer derived 'wholly or mainly' from the 'real' food if the amount of artificial flavour is increased. A further difficulty arises with the use of so-called 'nature-identical' flavours which are made up of chemical components present in the natural flavour and whose taste and smell are virtually indistinguishable from their natural counterparts (although sophisticated analytical techniques may detect minor compositional differences). We have been told that some manufacturers do not consider such flavours to be 'artificial' in the same way as other artificial flavours; while arguments can be made for this we do not accept them. For the purposes of distinguishing in the appropriate designation between the use of the 'real' food and a flavour, 'nature-identical' flavours should be grouped with other artificial flavours.

102. We think that it is important for the consumer for a distinction to be drawn between natural and artificial flavours and this is the intention of Regulation 11. Because of doubts about the wording 'wholly or mainly' and the different interpretations that can be placed upon them, there have been inevitable difficulties with enforcement of the Regulation and we are doubtful whether it is achieving its purpose. We therefore *recommend* that if the name of a food is used in an appropriate designation to indicate a specific flavour, that flavour must be derived *wholly* from the food indicated by that name. If the flavour is derived at all from any artificial flavour, the word 'flavour' must immediately follow the name of that food in letters of the same size, style and colour. No pictures of the food should be allowed where the flavour is not derived wholly from that food. Similarly the shape of a container should not suggest, say, a particular fruit if the flavour of that fruit is at all imparted by artificial flavour. We *recommend* accordingly. (The subject of container

shapes will be discussed further in our Second Report on Claims and Misleading Descriptions.)

103. *Use of the words 'flavour' and 'flavoured'*. Having recommended in paragraph 102 that the word 'flavour' *must* be used on food labels in certain circumstances, we are faced with the problem that the use of this word alone is unlikely to indicate to a consumer sufficiently clearly that artificial flavour has been used, which would seem to defeat the whole purpose of the requirement. The requirements of Regulation 11 aside, 'flavour' would seem to be used by manufacturers to indicate the use of artificial flavour (although there are exceptions to this) whereas 'flavoured' seems to be used principally where a food has been used to impart flavour eg 'flavoured with fresh oranges', 'strawberry flavoured' although, again, there may be exceptions. We doubt whether this distinction is clear to consumers even where further qualification of the description is made, such as 'flavoured with real X' or 'real X flavoured': in the latter type of example the word 'flavour' would seem to be more widely used than 'flavoured', which can only confuse the situation further. In the circumstances, and if our recommendation in paragraph 102 is to be effective, a much more positive distinction needs to be drawn on labels between the use of artificial flavour and the use of the 'real' food as the source of the flavour. In our view this will only be achieved by the use of the term 'artificial flavour' which without any shadow of doubt indicates that the flavour has not been derived from a 'natural' source in the sense understood by the public. We therefore *recommend* that where, in accordance with our recommendations in paragraph 102, a food is described as 'X flavour' as part of the appropriate designation, the words 'contains artificial flavour' should appear on the label in close proximity to the appropriate designation in letters of the same size, style and colour. The use of this phrase should remove any possible ambiguity about the use of the word 'flavour' and should be immediately understandable to the consumer. We would define 'artificial flavour' as any flavouring substance which is not derived exclusively from the food named in the appropriate designation as imparting a specific flavour. This recommendation would obviate the need to distinguish any further between 'flavour' and 'flavoured'.

104. Our recommendations above should help to resolve some of the difficulties with Regulation 11 which have been drawn to our attention. We recognise that these recommendations are more stringent than the existing requirements and that, for instance, where food with a particularly bland flavour needs to be boosted with an artificial flavour the word 'flavour' will need to be used in the appropriate designation together with the statement 'contains artificial flavour' and no pictures of the natural food will be allowed. This is consistent with the definition of 'appropriate designation' in paragraph 40 above which requires an indication of the 'true nature' of the food. If, for instance, the labelling of a product containing strawberries places emphasis on the presence of strawberries, but the flavour is not derived wholly from the fruit and artificial flavour is used, we consider an appropriate designation which did not indicate this would not indicate the 'true nature' of the food.

The consumer could be misled under these circumstances unless the use of artifical flavour is drawn to his attention more clearly than mere ingredient listing would achieve.

105. *Use of the word 'chocolate'.* It has been drawn to our attention in representations that in normal trade practice chocolate flavour is imparted by the addition of cocoa solids (usually as cocoa powder): chocolate is not used and the flavour is not therefore derived 'wholly or mainly' from chocolate. In accordance with Regulation 11 it should be described as cocoa or as 'chocolate flavour' and not 'chocolate' unqualified. 'Chocolate ice-cream' and 'chocolate sponge' are examples of foods which in theory do not comply with the Regulations.

106. The use of cocoa powder to impart 'chocolate' flavour has been recognised for many years by a Code of Practice [24] issued by the former Local Authorities' Joint Advisory Committee on Food Standards (LAJAC), since reconstituted as the Local Authorities' Co-ordinating Body on Trading Standards (LACOTS). The Code, agreed between enforcement authorities and the baking industry, deals with the use of the word 'chocolate' in flour confectionery and allows the word to be used provided a product contains not less than 3 per cent of dry non-fat cocoa solids in the moist crumb. We also examined the subject in our 1974 Report on Chocolate-Flavour Coatings and Fillings[25]. In paragraph 9 of that Report it was recommended that 2.5% of non-fat cocoa solids was in general sufficient to characterise foods with the word 'chocolate' in their names, other than chocolate itself. We consider that because of its well established usage, the use of the word 'chocolate' to refer to cocoa solids is acceptable and we do not think that the consumer will be prejudiced by its continued usage. We therefore *recommend* that the word 'chocolate' be allowed in legislation to be used in the name of any food if that food contains not less than 2.5 per cent non-fat cocoa solids. If less, the words 'flavoured with cocoa solids' or a similar statement would have to be used.

107. *Food Additives and Contaminants Committee Report on the Review of Flavourings in Food*[26]. We have noted the recommendations made by the Food Additives and Contaminants Committee in its 1976 Report that all flavourings for use in food should be controlled by a single permitted list and we have also noted that for the purpose of such control categories of flavourings may be different from those we have described. Our recommendations do not however conflict with this difference of approach.

---

[24]Local Authorities' Joint Advisory Committee on Food Standards:
Code of Practice No 1 — Use of the word 'Chocolate' in Flour Confectionery: 1963

[25]Food Standards Committee: Report on Chocolate-Flavour Coatings and Fillings: FSC/REP/E2: MAFF 1974

[26]Food Additives and Contaminants Committee: Report on the Review of Flavourings in Food: FAC/REP/22: HMSO 1976

108. *Proposed EEC enabling directive on flavourings.* We understand that discussions are taking place in Brussels with a view to drawing up proposals for an enabling directive to control flavourings when used as additives in food or when sold as such. Because these discussions are at an early stage we cannot comment on the extent to which our recommendations might be affected.

IV SPECIAL REQUIREMENTS FOR PARTICULAR FOODS

Butchers' meat and offal (excluding poultry)

109.   In the following paragraphs we use the expression 'butchers' meat' as a convenient term to include fresh, frozen or chilled meat derived from the usual meat animals other than poultry. Our general labelling recommendations in paragraphs 50 and 94 will mean that all foods, whether prepacked or non-prepacked, will have to be identified by an *appropriate designation*. As referred to in paragraph 95, however, we consider that certain foods, because of their importance, merit additional requirements in relation to the descriptions to be applied. For butchers' meat (other than poultry) we consider that a general requirement to specify the *appropriate designation* if narrowly interpreted to mean only the type of meat, e.g. pork, beef, may not always be sufficient to ensure that the consumer is provided with sufficiently detailed information on which to base a fair and informed choice. We therefore *recommend* that the *appropriate designation* required for both prepacked and non-prepacked butcher's meat should include an indication of the true name of the cut or joint as appropriate. Poultry and poultry meat are discussed in paragraph 122 below. We also *recommend* that the meaning of 'cut' be extended to include indications of use which are more generic than anatomically specific such as 'braising steak', 'stewing beef', but which if correctly applied are as useful to the consumer. These however can be abused as for example when meat of a quality which needs the most careful handling to roast satisfactorily is prepared as a roll and sold as 'roasting beef'; in this instance an anatomical cut description would give a better indication of the suitability of use. Where any doubt or ambiguity arises therefore there would be advantage in labelling with a 'name of cut' in anatomical terms as well as an indication of use and we *recommend* accordingly. The provision of this information will enable a consumer to exercise the same choice whether buying butchers' meat prepacked or non-prepacked. With non-prepacked items it will reduce the possibility of 'passing-off' since enforcement can be greatly facilitated if a written rather than a verbal statement is used when selling a particular cut or joint of meat. The reduction in instances of 'passing-off' brought about by the introduction of similar controls on fish names by the 1970 Labelling of Food Regulations supports our views in relation to labelling butchers' meat. We *recommend* however that the requirement to give an *appropriate designation* should not apply to butchers' meat and offal which may be on the shop premises but which is waiting to be cut or prepared for display. It should apply only to meat and offal 'exposed for sale in a display area'. This requirement is parallel to that for displaying the price under the Price Marking (Meat) Order 1977 discussed in paragraph 115 below.

110.   We also *recommend* that, to take account of any difficulties in establishing the full *appropriate designation* to be applied, the name of the cut or joint to be applied should be listed in a code of practice rather than in regulations (we understand that such a code is being drawn up jointly by the

Institute of Meat and the Meat and Livestock Commission). We consider that this is preferable to a rigid list of names in regulations, which could not take account of the many regional variations in names, developments in cutting techniques etc. We consider the declaration of the true name of the cut or joint of meat as being desirable as a matter of principle: we doubt that there will be any difficulties with such a requirement which cannot be overcome by the trade or be amenable to reasonable regional variations in practice.

111. Under our recommendations in paragraph 109 above, a term such as 'mince' would probably be acceptable since the recommended definition of *'appropriate designation'* in paragraph 42 includes common or usual names which are not misleading. 'Mince' used to describe minced beef would be a common or usual name for this purpose. Where 'mince' has been used traditionally to describe minced beef containing offal such as heart, it may similarly be argued that this is still the common or usual name by virtue of its traditional usage. If such a product were to be described as 'minced beef', it is probably already misleading under Section 6 of the Food and Drugs Act 1955 since it purports to be a specific description rather than a common or usual name (which does not necessarily have to be, and is not usually, specific). A comment on this question, essentially in similar terms, will appear in our forthcoming Report on Meat Products.

112. We consider that the origin of butchers' meat and offal is also of importance to the consumer. We are aware, however, that declaration of the country of origin of all produce is subject to the Trade Descriptions Acts 1968 and 1972[27] and therefore outside our terms of reference. We concluded nevertheless that we should comment on an aspect of consumer information which is of particular importance in this area. The country of origin of meat has often in the past been related to the way meat has been processed and stored; thus meat from Australasia will probably have been frozen and meat from Argentina chilled. We believe that the other labelling requirements which we are recommending for butchers' meat and offal will deal with real differences rather than the presumed differences related to country of origin and that there is therefore no need for any specific requirement. Article 3.1(7) of the EEC Food Labelling Directive requires that all prepacked food must carry an indication of origin or provenance where omission might mislead the consumer to a material degree. We believe that this is an important provision for the consumer and should similarly apply to non-prepacked butchers' meat and offal.

113. We also examined a suggestion that a declaration of 'chilled' or 'frozen' accompanying butchers' meat and offal might be a necessary requirement for the information of the consumer. The conclusion we have reached, however, is that only the relatively small proportion of meat and offal which has been frozen (ie below $-2°C$) and then sold thawed needs to bear any sort of

---

[27]Trade Descriptions Act 1968; 1969 C 29
Trade Description Act 1972; 1972 C 34

declaration. The process of freezing tends to affect adversely the structure of meat and offal and hence the quality will deteriorate each time freezing takes place. Ideally therefore meat and offal should not be re-frozen once it has thawed. This is particularly true in the home, where it may often be difficult to achieve ideal freezing conditions during any re-freezing process. There may well also be difficulties through the possibility of contamination before re-freezing. It is important that consumers are made aware of the problems encountered when re-freezing meat and offal in the home and they should always be informed where meat and offal sold as fresh has been previously frozen and thawed for sale. We therefore *recommend* that butchers' meat and offal which has been frozen and then thawed for retail sale should be labelled or ticketed as appropriate to indicate this. Meat which is evidently still frozen (ie displayed in a freezer cabinet) would not need to comply but frozen meat placed in a chill cabinet to thaw must be treated as frozen and thawed meat. It is not possible to estimate with precision the quantity of meat and offal likely to be affected by our recommendations. It can however be concluded that relatively small proportions of beef and pork are likely to be sold frozen or thawed after frozen storage: the proportion of lamb which has been frozen is probably over 50%. Although this is usually identifiable by its country of origin — New Zealand or Australia — if thawed the requirement recommended above is clearly needed.

114.   We do not consider that there is a similar need to identify meat which has been chilled: virtually all carcase meat is cooled down to near 0°C following slaughter, principally as a hygiene measure. If all such meat were required to be described as 'chilled' it might falsely imply that it was inferior to 'fresh'. Indeed, for all practical purposes, from the point of view of both retailer and consumer it is 'fresh' meat.

115.   *The Price Marking (Meat) Order 1977*[28]. We have been told that under this Order (which came into operation on 1 March 1978) it is probable that where the price of fresh, frozen or chilled meat is given on a separate list of named cuts, eg on a wall in the shop, rather than on a ticket attached to the meat, the cuts described must be identified. This is due to the requirement that price indications must be 'easily recognizable' when not on the meat. Our recommendations are unlikely to conflict with any of the requirements of this Order.

Food which has been frozen and then thawed for retail sale
116.   In making recommendations in relation to meat and offal which has been frozen and then thawed for retail sale (paragraph 113) we examined representations that all food (eg bread) which has undergone this process should be so marked. We do not however consider that with these other foods freezing and thawing creates the same problems as with meat and offal. We do not know to what extent foods other than meat, offal and sausages (as referred

---

[28]SI 1977 No 1412 (applies to Great Britain).

43

to in paragraph 44 of our 1972 Report on Date Marking) are frozen and thawed and we have not been told that any difficulties occur or that consumers are prejudiced in any way. In the circumstances we make no recommendation other than that in paragraph 113.

Fresh fruit and vegetables

117.   The 1970 Labelling of Food Regulations do not at present apply to the sale of non-prepacked fresh fruit and vegetables although when prepacked they are required to bear an appropriate designation and the name and address of the packer or labeller etc on the label. Certain exemptions to the latter provisions are provided by Regulations 6(2) and (3) for a retailer selling on the premises where prepacking was carried out or from his own delivery van (see paragraphs 76-82 and 85). Our recommendations in paragraphs 50 and 94 for all prepacked and non-prepacked food to be identified by an *appropriate designation* will ensure a more consistent approach in the future. With fresh fruit and vegetables however, as with fresh meat and offal, we consider that the *appropriate designation* may need in many instances to be amplified by more detailed information. We consider that a declaration of variety such as 'Granny Smith' or 'Conference' should also be required since this will be important to the consumer in relation to produce such as apples or pears where different varieties exhibit different eating qualities and will be purchased on this basis. A declaration of variety would not however be necessary for all produce since with some a description such as 'carrots' would seem to be sufficient. A declaration of variety in such instances would not be meaningful to most consumers and so would be of little or no value. Any recommendation for variety declaration by this Committee would need therefore to relate only to specific types of fruit and vegetables where variety had been identified as playing an important part in consumer choice. The existence of EEC grading regulations for horticultural produce however would appear to render such a general recommendation unnecessary and we discuss this in paragraphs 118-120 below.

118.   EEC grading regulations[29] apply to most prepacked and non-prepacked fresh fruit and vegetables (other than potatoes). These regulations require that those fruit and vegetables which are subject to grading requirements and offered for retail sale must be accompanied by details of the origin of the produce, the quality class and (for some produce) the variety. The information must be on the label attached to the bulk container whether the contents are prepacked or not. When sold by retail direct from the container, it is sufficient if these details are clearly visible to purchasers. Fruit and vegetables on offer for sale by retail away from the original bulk container must be accompanied by a display card setting out the necessary information if the latter is not shown on the label of a retail prepack. It should be noted that there is no general requirement to indicate the variety of all produce and only the grade and origin must always be given. The variety declaration requirement is additionally inconsistent in that it relates only to particular classes of

---

[29]Council Regulation (EEC) No 1035/72 O J Special Edition 1972 (II)

particular produce eg the variety of applies is required to be declared only for the Extra and Class 1 produce, for the remaining classes the required information relates solely to quality class and origin.

119. Despite the inconsistencies in variety declaration identified in paragraph 118 above, we consider that the EEC grading regulations are a useful measure and we would not wish therefore to make any recommendations in relation to produce governed by those regulations. We understand that the inconsistencies are being examined with a view to the United Kingdom seeking necessary changes and in the circumstances we do not consider that recommendations by this Committee on this particular aspect of food labelling would be appropriate. We note that our recommendations in paragraphs 50 and 94 would apply to fresh fruit and vegetables and that, if implemented, there would be an over-lap between the requirements of any future UK labelling legislation and the EEC grading regulations and this might cause difficulties, particularly with non-prepacked produce. We therefore *recommend* that any produce covered by EEC grading regulations should be exempt from any future labelling legislation, even if this means that not all fruit and vegetables where variety is important will be required to declare this. Exemption from labelling legislation would seem to be preferable to attempting to impose a further set of requirements which could be very confusing at the retail level.

120. With produce not covered by the EEC regulations there is no such legislative difficulty and variety declaration could be applied in practice. We consider however that such a declaration is only justifiable as a statutory requirement for *potatoes* and *melons* and we *recommend* accordingly. Any other produce (excluding that covered by EEC grading regulations) will be subject to our general recommendations in paragraphs 50 and 94 and would only be required to bear an *appropriate designation*. We have noted that melons may eventually be subject to EEC grading regulations. If these or potatoes or any other produce become subject to such regulations they will need to be exempted from UK labelling legislation as we have recommended above.

Eggs and poultry

121. There are separate EEC requirements for the labelling of eggs. Regulation (EEC) No. 2772/75[30] on marketing standards for eggs requires the following information to be shown on prepacked eggs:

(a) the name or trade name and address of the packer or the undertaking on whose behalf the eggs were packed;

(b) the registered number of the packing station;

(c) the quality and weight grading;

(d) the number of eggs packed;

---

[30]O.J. No L282 1.11.75 (implemented in the UK as the Eggs Marketing Standards Regulations 1973 (SI 1973 No 15 as amended by SI 1978 No 1248))

(e) the date or week number of packing; and

(f) where appropriate, particulars of refrigeration or the method of preservation.

Large boxes used for transporting eggs, including those containing small prepacks, are required to carry all the above information. Non-prepacked graded eggs must be accompanied by a label or display card showing at least the quality class and weight grade. A producer selling his own ungraded eggs direct to the consumer at the farm gate, door-to-door or at a local public market is however exempt from the Regulations. All these requirements are not inconsistent with the recommendations in this Report.

122. Labelling requirements for poultry are at present under discussion as part of a draft EEC regulation on marketing standards for poultrymeat. These will include prepacked and non-prepacked carcases and cuts but the information to be required on labels has not been finally agreed. In addition, as discussed in our 1978 Report on Water in Food, EEC Regulation 2967/76[31] which limits the water content of frozen and deep frozen chickens, hens and cocks, is due to come fully into force on 1 January 1980 and will introduce certain labelling requirements. Individual and bulk packs of chicken treated with polyphosphates will be required to bear 'a clear and legible description of the treatment applied'. Poultry not complying with the Regulation may still be marketed provided it carries 'an appropriate description on the individual and bulk packaging'. The wording to be required on labels for such poultry has also yet to be decided. The introduction of all these requirements will mean that in future prepacked and non-prepacked poultry will be required to be accompanied by information not inconsistent with our recommendations for meat and offal in paragraph 109 above. We therefore make no specific recommendations for poultry and poultry meat in this Report.

Fish

123. We examined the need to distinguish between fresh and thawed-out frozen fish as referred to in paragraph 83 of our 1964 Report on Food Labelling (referred to in paragraph 92 of this Report). Fish differs from meat in that unless frozen and stored at −20°C or below within a short time of catching, the quality will deteriorate rapidly. It is therefore important for the consumer that fish other than that for immediate consumption should be quickly and correctly frozen as soon as possible. The complexities involved in freezing at sea, thawing, filleting and re-freezing however present circumstances where any requirements for labelling to indicate this history may be impracticable and perhaps inappropriate. In particular, we would wish to avoid any change in labelling requirements which might discourage the purchase of fish which has been frozen at sea, which, if correctly handled in subsequent distribution, may well be of superior quality to nominally 'fresh' fish which has not been frozen at any stage. In the circumstances we consider that the question of labelling fish as having been frozen and thawed should

---

[31]O.J. No L339/1 8.12.76 as amended

more appropriately be the subject of a special, separate review and we therefore make no recommendations concerning fish labelling in this Report other than those on the names to be applied to fish in paragraphs 205-238 below.

Acetic acid (Regulation 12 and Schedule 5)

124.   Acetic acid is permitted for use in food by the Miscellaneous Additives in Food Regulations 1974 as amended[32]. No restrictions are placed on its use other than those afforded by the general provisions of the Food and Drugs Acts. The labelling of concentrated acetic acid is however controlled by Regulation 12 of the 1970 Labelling of Food Regulations. The Regulation provides that no person, other than a pharmacist or an 'authorised seller of poisons', may sell for human consumption any prepacked concentrated acetic acid or solution of acetic acid containing more than 150 grams per litre of acetic acid unless:

(a)   it is described as 'concentrated solution of acetic acid (x) per cent', the description being completed by inserting the appropriate figures at (x); and

(b)   the words 'Dangerous — not to be used unless diluted' appear on the label.

Paragraph 10 of Schedule 5 requires that the warning in (b) above appear in red characters not less than 3 millimetres high on a white ground. From 1 March 1979 acetic acid of more than 25% concentration by weight has been subject to special labelling under the Packaging and Labelling of Dangerous Substances Regulations 1978[33].

125.   We sought the views of the Food Additives and Contaminants Committee (FACC) on whether there was a need on safety grounds to continue these labelling controls. FACC concluded that since concentrated acetic acid is a much stronger acid than many consumers might expect and as the existing labelling provisions were not known to have caused any difficulties, it would be a sensible precaution to continue the existing requirements. We agree with this view and *recommend* that the existing provisions be retained. We doubt however whether they are appropriate for inclusion in food labelling legislation and we therefore *recommend* that consideration be given to their inclusion in other legislation such as the Packaging and Dangerous Substances Regulations 1978. Any new provisions will need to change the term 'authorised seller of poisons' to 'persons lawfully conducting a retail pharmacy business' to be consistent with Section 69 of the Medicines Act 1968.

Dried or dehydrated foods (Regulation 14)

126.   Regulation 14 of the 1970 Labelling of Food Regulations follows closely

---

[32]England and Wales SI 1974 No 1121 ⎱ The amendments to these Regulations are
Scotland SI 1974 No 1338 (S116) ⎰ not relevant to the labelling of acetic acid.
Northern Ireland SR (NI) 1974 No 196

[33]England, Wales and Scotland SI 1978 No 209. There are no equivalent Northern Ireland Regulations.

recommendations made in paragraph 98 of our 1966 Report on Claims and Misleading Descriptions. The Regulation applies to any food consisting of *one main ingredient* which is dried or dehydrated, and which is customarily sold either before and after having been dried or dehydrated. Such food must be given an appropriate designation which includes the word 'dried', 'dehydrated' or 'desiccated'. Dried foods traditionally sold by a name which does not include the words 'dried', 'dehydrated' or 'desiccated' and to which such name has been 'customarily and exclusively' applied, such as prunes, are exempt from this requirement (Regulation 14 (4)). 'Instant tea' is permitted as an appropriate designation (without the inclusion of the word 'dried' etc) for any dried extract of tea, provided the words 'soluble solids of tea' are included in the list of ingredients (Regulation 14(3)). 'Instant coffee' is permitted by the 1967 Coffee and Coffee Product Regulations (see footnote (4)).

127.   We consider that Regulation 14 is in general operating satisfactorily and should be retained. We have noted that Article 5(3) of the EEC Food Labelling Directive requires that the name under which a product is sold should include or be accompanied by particulars of the physical condition of the food or the specific treatment undergone (eg powdered, freeze-dried, deep-frozen, concentrated, smoked) in all instances 'where omission of such information could create confusion in the mind of the purchaser'. It is not clear whether this provision, once enacted in UK law, will always apply in the same circumstances as Regulation 14 and we believe that, to avoid possible confusion, there is a need to maintain existing UK requirements. We *recommend* accordingly.

Dry mixes (Regulation 15)

128.   Dry mixes, which are sold to be made up into complete foods such as cakes, are discussed in paragraph 99 of our 1966 Report on Claims. We recommended that these should be described as 'X mix', 'X' being the name of the product that the mix will make with the addition of water. We also recommended that if any ingredient apart from water were required, this should be stated in close association with the designation by adding the words 'Add Y', 'Y' being the name of the ingredient or ingredients to be added.

129.   Regulation 15 of the 1970 Labelling of Food Regulations (as amended by the 1972 Labelling of Food (Amendment) Regulations) reflects our 1966 recommendations only in part. Although there is no requirement to describe products as 'X mix', a statement of the ingredients needed other than water to make up the mix is required. If substances other than water must be added to a dry mix to make it into another food and that other food is mentioned on the label of the dry mix, the substance to be added must be shown clearly, legibly and in immediate proximity to the appropriate designation, in the form 'Add Y'. The statement need only be made in immediate proximity to the appropriate designation given in accordance with Regulation 5: it does not have to be given every time the appropriate designation is referred to on the label.

130. Regulation 15 also applies to advertisements. In those presented other than orally, the substances other than water that have to be added must be stated (along with a statement that they have to be added) clearly, legibly, conspicuously and in immediate proximity to the most prominent statement relating to the final product. In advertisements presented orally, the substances other than water to be added, and the fact that they have to be added, must be mentioned audibly and clearly at least once.

131. Regulation 15(4)(a) exempts from the requirements of Regulation 15 foods which can be made up either with water alone or with water and/or other ingredients. The wording is such that the intention only to exempt foods for which the addition of water alone or of water and other ingredients are alternatives at the choice of the purchaser is not unambiguously phrased. This should be clarified in future regulations. Custard powder and blancmange powder are specifically exempted by Regulation 15(4)(b).

132. We have examined Regulation 15 in the light of our 1966 recommendations and representations received. The provisions appear generally to be operating satisfactorily and we consider they should be retained. We are concerned however that the ingredient(s) necessary to make up the complete food from the dry mix may not always be sufficiently conspicuous on the label, in spite of the general clarity requirements in the Regulation. To ensure that these ingredients are always given sufficient prominence, the letters in the statement 'Add Y' should be at least three-quarters the height of the largest letter (other than an initial letter) in the appropriate designation. With this one change, we *recommend* that Regulation 15 be retained in future legislation. Article 3.1(8) of the EEC Food Labelling Directive requires that a food be marked with instructions for use 'when it would be impossible to make appropriate use of the foodstuff in the absence of such instructions' and Article 4(2) makes provision for the maintenance of national provisions applicable to specified foods. The retention of Regulation 15 as modified will therefore accord with the provisions of the Directive.

133. We have not recommended, as we did in 1966, that dry mixes should be described as 'X Mix'. For most such foods the requirement to given an appropriate designation should be sufficient to ensure that this is done. We have noted however that dried soups are not often described on labels as 'soup mix'. For clarity, therefore, and reiterating the views expressed in paragraph 16 of our Report on Soups[34], we *recommend* that the appropriate designation for dried soup should be 'soup mix', suitably qualified to indicate the type of soup.

134. We have examined the sale of dry mixes where none of the major ingredients of the final product is present, such as those to be added to meat and vegetables to produce stews and casseroles. We are concerned that some of

---

[34]Food Standards Committee Report on Soups: FSC/REP/52: HMSO 1968

the descriptions used may be misleading: we have been told of a product described as 'a mix for *Coq-au-Vin*' which contained neither *'Coq'* nor *'Vin'!* Clearly such a description does not convey any indication of the 'true nature of the food' as is required by the definition of appropriate designation in Regulation 3(1). Most of these products are mixtures of seasonings and/or flavourings to be added to a product to impart the flavour of a specific dish. Manufacturers clearly wish to attract the cachet of the name of a traditional dish to a product which does not contain any of the traditional ingredients. There is a consequential need for a measure of regulation in the way these products are described. We therefore *recommend* that dry mixes where none of the major ingredients of the final product are present and which are to be added, for instance, to meat and/or vegetables to produce stews, casseroles, etc should be described as 'seasoning mix' or some other similarly unambiguous description. It should be noted that many products serving a similar role are now marketed in the form of a canned sauce. The descriptions used for these do not seem to have created difficulties so that we do not recommend any specific control.

135.   We have considered Regulation 15(4)(b), which exempts custard powder from the requirement to state 'add milk' on the label, in the light of the recent appearance on the market of complete custard powders requiring the addition only of water. We have, however, no knowledge of consumers experiencing difficulties in differentiating between these newer products and 'traditional' custard powders. Until such time as difficulties occur, the exemption for custard powder should remain. We *recommend* accordingly.

Intoxicating and other liquor (Regulations 16, 17 and Schedule 5)

136.   The general requirements of Regulation 5 of the 1970 Regulations do not apply to the labelling of intoxicating liquor, this being controlled by Regulations 16 and 17. Prepacked intoxicating liquor sold by retail must be labelled with an appropriate designation which includes the country of origin. The name and address of the labeller or packer etc (as in Regulation 5(3)) and certain additional declarations are also required. 'Intoxicating liquor' is defined in Regulation 2(1) as:

> '. . . . . . spirits, wine, beer, cider, perry, British wine and any other fermented, distilled or spirituous liquor but (apart from cider and perry) does not include any liquor for the sale of which by wholesale no excise licence is required'.

137.   *EEC Wine Regulations*[35]. These Regulations control the labelling of *light wines* (quality wine produced in a specified EEC region, table wine (non-quality EEC wine) and third country wine) and we have been told that they override the requirements of Regulations 16 and 17 of the 1970 Labelling of Food Regulations relating to these products. In these circumstances we think

---

[35]Council Regulations (EEC) No 337/79 OJ No L54 5.3.79
Council Regulation (EEC) No 355/79 OJ No L54 5.3.79
Commission Regulation (EEC) No 1608/76 as amended. OJ No L183 8.7.76

that the 1970 Regulations need to be suitably amended to clarify the matter. 'Wine' is defined in Annex II to EEC Regulation 337/79 as 'the product obtained exclusively from the total or partial alcoholic fermentation of fresh grapes, whether or not crushed, or of grape musts' and the use of the word 'wine' is prohibited for other products except under certain conditions stipulated in Article 45.2 of EEC Regulations 355/79. The circumstances in which the word 'wine' may be applied to other products, such as 'British Wine', 'Irish Wine' etc, made from grape must, require amendment of UK Regulations as discussed in paragraph 152. Further EEC regulations covering sparkling and semi-sparkling wines (whether aerated or not) and liqueur wines are likely to be enacted and these will similarly override the provisions of the 1970 Labelling of Food Regulations. An EEC directive on alcohol tables[36] will make it necessary from 1 January 1980 for alcoholic strength to be expressed as 'per cent alcohol by volume' ('% vol'). Amendment of the Labelling Regulations will be necessary to take this into account. We discuss the terms of all these amendments when examining the relevant provisions in the following paragraphs.

138. *Appropriate designation.* Regulations 16(1) and (2)(b) require that the labels of intoxicating liquor bear an appropriate designation which must include, or be accompanied by, a reference to the country or countries of origin of the liquor expressed as a noun or an adjective. Regulation 16(3) requires that, in the appropriate designation statement,

'(a) no geographical name shall be applied to intoxicating liquor produced in any country or locality other than that indicated by the name unless it is the name of a distinctive type of intoxicating liquor; and

(b) no description or geographical name which implies or suggests that an intoxicating liquor is a distinctive type of intoxicating liquor which has originated in a particular country or locality should be applied to any such liquor produced elsewhere than in that country or locality unless that description or name is immediately preceded by an adjective in identical lettering indicating the true country or locality of origin'.

139.   The requirements of Regulations 16(2)(b) and 16(3) are very similar to those of the Labelling of Food Order 1953, the effects of which we discussed fully in paragraphs 106 to 111 of our 1964 Report on Food Labelling. We recognise that if written today the analysis in those paragraphs would not use wine as an example since EEC law has now superseded UK labelling legislation. Nevertheless, the principles enunciated remain relevant to other intoxicating liquor and, with this reservation, we consider that paragraphs 108-111 are therefore worthy of repetition in this Report as follows:

'108.   The effect of this definition (of appropriate designation) depends entirely on the meaning given to the expression "distinctive type of intoxicating liquor". This has not been decided by the courts, but the definition implies that some geographical names are the names of

---

[36]Council Directive (EEC) No 766/76 OJ No L262 27.9.76.

distinctive types of intoxicating liquor. It seems impossible to discover any criterion — other than usage — for deciding which are and which are not and therefore the definition does not protect any geographical name which could possibly be regarded as generic, if any wine-producer in any country wanted to use it, provided he preceded it by his own country's name in adjectival form. Two important exceptions to this situation are "Port" and "Madeira" which are already protected by the Anglo-Portuguese Commercial Treaty Acts of 1914 and 1916.

'109.   It can be argued that the use of a geographical name for wine which is not produced in the area indicated by the name is misleading, even if that name is qualified adjectivally by a different geographical name: that the nature and quality of a wine are due to a number of factors such as soil, climate and traditional methods which are peculiar to the district of origin and, though a wine of a similar type may be produced elsewhere, it should not be regarded as the same wine: and that wine sold as a "Ruritanian Graves" for instance, is simply not a Graves but, so long as geographical names for wines are not protected, it is not easy for those who are not experts to understand that wines of a different nature can be sold under the same name because they are of a similar type and that the adjectival qualifications are all important.

'110.   Against this view it may be argued, firstly, that many famous wine names derived from the geographical names of long established wine-producing areas have become generally established as the names of types of wines, and have been used unchallenged as names for wines from other countries, in the same way as Cheddar has become the name of a variety of cheese made throughout the world and no longer solely at Cheddar; secondly, that imported "must" is used to supplement the indigenous grapejuice and that imported wine is added to wines bearing geographical names: and thirdly, that it is accepted practice to fortify certain wines with spirit, and that, in this case, the process of production is at least as important as the origin of the raw materials.

'111.   The question of international agreement on the nomenclature of intoxicating liquors is under consideration by a Committee of Experts on the Production and Marketing of Vine Products and Spirits set up by the Council of Europe. The United Kingdom is represented on this Committee which we understand is trying to work out a system for the protection of geographical names of wines and spirits that will be acceptable to producing and consuming countries. Meanwhile, under the general provisions of the Food and Drugs Act 1955, it could be argued that the sale of a wine from an area other than from the geographical location, in response to a request for "a wine from that location", would be "not of the nature, or not of the substance, or not of the quality demanded". In view of this and of the efforts being made to secure international agreement on nomenclature we do not recommend any changes in the present provisions of the Labelling of Food Order on the use of geographical names. The country of origin, of course, has already to be declared by the present Labelling Order.'

The function of the Committee of Experts referred to in paragraph 111 of our 1964 Report has, we understand, been superseded by current regulation-making procedures within the EEC.

140.   EEC Regulations 355/79 and 1608/76 (as amended) override the provisions of Regulation 16 concerning details to be included in descriptions on labels including the need to bear an appropriate designation. The effects of this and forthcoming EEC regulations on the control and use of names applied to intoxicating liquor are likely to be significant. In the circumstances any changes in appropriate designation requirements now may be premature. The existing provisions of Regulation 16(2)(b) and (3) seem to have caused little difficulty in operation and they afford the consumer a degree of protection. Although we have some reservations as to the degree of protection afforded, as discussed in our 1964 Report on Food Labelling, we *recommend* that the existing provisions be retained in respect of alcoholic liquor not controlled by EEC regulations.

141.   *Name and address.* Regulation 16(2)(a) requires prepacked intoxicating liquor to carry particulars of the name and address of the packer or labeller etc as in Regulation 5(3) and as discussed in paragraphs 83-86 above. Special provisions applicable to some vintage wines are also discussed in paragraphs 83-84. Subject to the requirements of EEC wine regulations we *recommend* that Regulation 16(2)(a) be retained.

142.   *Additional declarations.* Other information to be given on labels, such as a declaration of alcohol content, is required by Regulation 16(4), but only in relation to intoxicating liquor other than beer, cider, perry and wine obtained by the fermentation of the juice of grapes but no other fruit, which wine has not been subject to any process so as to alter its character. (Article 4(2) of the EEC Food Labelling Directive would permit these additional declarations to continue). The effects of the exclusion from control by Regulation 16(4) of wine which has *not* been subject to any process so as to alter its character means that only where the essential character of wine has been changed will it be subject to additional declarations on the label, to draw these changes to the attention of the consumer. If no such changes have taken place the product need only be labelled in accordance with the general requirements of Regulation 16(2). Beer, cider and perry are also only subject to the general requirements, special declarations such as alcohol content presumably being considered inappropriate when the 1970 Regulations were made. We have, however, made recommendations for the labelling of beer in our 1977 Report on Beer and we make recommendations below for additional labelling requirements which are relevant to cider and perry.

143.   The additional declarations required by Regulation 16(4) cover a wide range of intoxicating liquors. Undistilled fermented liquor not made from grapes must carry a declaration of its fruit base and minimum alcohol content

(Regulations 16(4)(a) and (b)). Undistilled fermented liquor not derived wholly or partly from fruit must carry the statement 'not made from fruit' together with the minimum alcohol content (Regulation 16(4)(c)). Intoxicating liquor is deemed not to be derived from any fruit present only in insignificant quantities: 'fruit' includes rhubarb (Regulation 16(6)). Brandy (other than that which has fallen below 65 per cent proof spirit (alcoholic strength 37% vol)[37] only through maturing in cask), gin, rum and whisky of less than 65 per cent proof spirit must bear the minimum alcohol content preceded by the words "Diluted with water to not less than . . . . . ." or "Understrength. Not less than . . . . . ." (Regulation 16(4)(d)). Any other intoxicating liquor to which the Regulation applies need only declare the minimum alcohol content (Regulation 16(4)(e)). The declaration of the minimum alcohol content in all instances, except for brandy which has fallen below 65 per cent proof spirit only through maturing in cask, may be expressed as either 'per cent alcohol by volume' or 'per cent proof spirit'. However for brandy, gin, rum, vodka and whisky of not less than 65 per cent proof spirit and any other intoxicating liquor of not less than 40 per cent proof spirit (alcoholic strength 23% vol)[37] a declaration expressed as 'X degrees proof' is sufficient (Regulation 16(5)). Brandy which has fallen below 65 per cent proof spirit only through maturing in cask must carry a declaration of the minimum alcohol content either as 'per cent proof spirit' or 'degrees proof'.

144.   Manner of marking is set out in paragraph 11 of Schedule 5: all declarations required by Regulation 16(4) must appear within a surrounding line and no matter other than that required by Regulation 16(4) may appear within that surrounding line. The height of the shortest letter or numeral in any declaration required by Regulation 16(4) or 16(5) must be not less than 3mm: this need only be 2mm for bottles smaller than the normal half bottle.

145.   *Declaration of alcohol content*[38]. As referred to in paragraph 137, EEC Directive 766/76 on alcohol tables requires that from 1 January 1980 alcoholic strength must be expressed as percentage alcohol by volume (% vol) (the Alcohol Tables Regulations 1979[39] now refer). From that date, the alternative forms of alcohol content declaration used in Regulation 16(4) — 'per cent proof spirit' and 'degrees proof' — may no longer be permitted on their own. (The difference between '% vol' and 'proof spirit' is explained in paragraph 113 of our 1964 Report on Food Labelling.) All such references in the Regulation may therefore need to be appropriately amended. We have previously recommended this change in paragraph 113 of our 1964 Report and consider it a further step forward in providing greater information for the consumer: percentage alcohol by volume is a much simpler method of calculating alcohol content and consequently will be much easier to understand and less misleading.

---

[37]The precise equivalents of 65% and 40% proof spirit are alcoholic strengths 37.18% vol and 22.92% vol respectively.

[38]The term 'alcoholic strength' is now more appropriate than 'alcoholic content' but since the latter is referred to in the 1970 Labelling of Food Regulations this term is used as appropriate throughout paragraphs 145 and 146.

[39]SI 1979 No 132 (applies to the United Kingdom).

146.   We think that there is in theory much in favour of *all* alcoholic drinks carrying a declaration of minimum alcohol content and are pleased to see that such declarations are beginning to appear even where there is no statutory requirement. We accept however that there are valid arguments against this proposition as it relates to some beverages, such as the possibility of beers being drunk purely for their alcohol content (which we discussed in our 1977 Report on Beer). We have therefore decided to follow a course which takes into account these points and also the need for some degree of equality of treatment between products which are in close competition. In our Report on Beer we discussed the idea of a minimum alcohol content declaration but recommended instead a declaration of original gravity. In this context we do not recommend a declaration of minimum alcohol content for cider and perry which we are told are close competitors of beer and of each other. Under EEC Regulation 355/79 a declaration of alcoholic strength in respect of light wines is optional, although until 31 August 1981 Member States may derogate from this and make it compulsory if they wish. Since the EEC Council of Ministers is to decide before 31 August 1981 on common arrangements that will apply after that date, we consider that it would be inappropriate to recommend that the UK take up now the derogation for the alcohol declaration for light wines. Nor do we consider that we can fairly recommend at this time that wines not covered by this Regulation should be required to declare alcohol content. Although we believe that as a matter of principle all alcoholic beverages should eventually be required to declare the alcohol content, in view of the circumstances outlined above we cannot at the present time recommend the introduction of such a general requirement. As a first move towards recognition of this general principle, however, we *recommend* that all beverages with an alcohol content in excess of 18% should declare the alcohol content. This would mean that some sherries and most ports as well as those beverages which are currently required to indicate their alcohol content would come under this rule in the future. We further *recommend* that, bearing in mind the general equity of treatment we would wish to see, the general principle of declaration for all intoxicating liquor should be recognised and eventually implemented. We note that under Article 6.3 of the EEC Food Labelling Directive in respect of beverages containing more than 1.2% by volume of alcohol, there is a possibility that rules for labelling these with the alcoholic strength may be determined within four years following notification of the Directive. This would seem to support our view.

147.   *Intoxicating liquor not made from fruit.* We are doubtful of the value of the declaration 'Not made from fruit' required by Regulation 16(4)(c) for undistilled fermented liquor not derived wholly or partly from fruit. Although this declaration may have been necessary at the time the control first appeared in legislation (1946) we consider that the requirement to give an appropriate designation such as 'parsnip wine' is sufficiently informative and we so *recommend.*

148.   *Understrength spirits.* Certain spirits of less than 65 per cent proof spirit must carry a special declaration on the label as described in paragraph 143

above and must be described (Regulation 17 (v)) as 'diluted', 'understrength' or some similar word, immediately preceding the name of the spirit in identical lettering. These provisions ensure that spirits below 65% proof spirit are appropriately labelled when sold. We understand however that there is now little sale of prepacked understrength spirits and detailed controls in labelling legislation would no longer seem to be required. The general provisions of Sections 2 and 6 of the Food and Drugs Acts should afford sufficient protection for the consumer in future and we therefore *recommend* that Regulations 16(4)(d) and 17(v) be deleted.

149. Section 3(4) of the Food and Drugs Act 1955 provides that in proceedings under Section 2 of the Act in respect of diluted whisky, brandy, rum and gin, it is a defence for the defendant to prove that the spirit had been diluted with water only and that its strength was still not lower than thirty-five degrees under proof (65° proof). This Section will need to be examined in the light of our recommendations: the current review of the Food and Drugs Acts now being undertaken by Government Departments will provide this opportunity. Its provisions would however seem more appropriate to specific legislation, rather than the general provisions of the Act.

150. *Declaration of ingredients.* We have already discussed the need for intoxicating liquor to carry a declaration of its ingredients in paragraph 155 of our 1977 Report on Beer and paragraphs 17 to 22 of our Report on Ingredient Listing. In paragraph 22 of the latter Report we recommended that, notwithstanding some of the practical difficulties involved, ingredients should be declared for all intoxicating liquor. In the context of special declarations for intoxicating liquor as discussed in paragraphs 142-149 above, an ingredients list is particularly helpful in understanding the nature of the food in that it will supplement the information provided in, for instance, the declaration of alcohol content. We would like to repeat strongly our view that intoxicating liquor should no longer remain exempt from an ingredient declaration. Nevertheless, we are aware that EEC law on wine labelling and the EEC Food Labelling Directive, which do not make ingredient listing compulsory for all alcoholic beverages, reflect relatively recent joint decisions by all Member States: it would consequently be unreasonable to expect a reversal of this agreement within a short space of time. The question of ingredient lists under the EEC Food Labelling Directive has however only been deferred, and rules have to be agreed within four years of notification of the Directive (Article 6.3 refers). We hope that this may provide an opportunity to move nearer to universal ingredient listing.

151. *Use of the word 'wine'.* Regulation 17 contains further requirements for the labelling *and advertising* of intoxicating and other liquors. (It should be noted that Regulation 16 discussed above only applies to labelling: advertisements are not covered.) Regulation 17(i) controls the use of the word 'wine' in that it prohibits the use of anything which indicates directly or indirectly that a liquor is or resembles or is a substitute for or has the flavour of wine unless it is derived from grapes and no other fruit. Regulation 17(ii)

further requires that if the word 'wine' is used in connection with any intoxicating liquor not derived from fruit or which is wholly or partly derived from fruit other than grapes, that word must be immediately preceded in identical lettering by a description of the fruit etc used. The descriptions 'Ginger Wine' and 'Orange Wine' are not, however, prevented: these traditional names have been used for many years to describe light wines flavoured with, but not derived from, ginger or orange.

152. Regulations 17(i) and (ii) will require amendment as a result of EEC limitation on the use of the word 'wine'. Under EEC Regulations 355/79 and 1608/76 (as amended) (relevant extracts from which are at Appendix 5), the word 'wine' may be used to describe products not falling within the EEC definition of 'wine' only for (a) products obtained by the fermentation of fruit other than grapes where the word is used as part of a composite name in conjunction with the name of the fruit used and (b) in other composite names including the word 'wine'. To avoid confusion between 'wine' as defined and these products, the word 'wine' may only be used in a composite name and never on its own and such a composite name must be clearly distinguishable from other information on the label. We consider that these requirements add little to the controls established for many years in the UK by Regulations 17(i) and (ii). We have no objection however to their introduction and if they improve the control on the possibility of misuse of the word 'wine' they must be welcomed as further protection for the consumer. When the changes to Regulation 17(i) and (ii) are made it will be important to ensure that the names of traditional products such as orange wine, ginger wine and elderberry wine can continue to be used. Provision should also be made to allow the continued sale of products such as home-made wine kits. We would not wish to see the availability of these reduced for the sake of protecting continental wine producers and we *recommend* accordingly.

153. *Sweetened liqueurs.* Regulation 17(iii) prohibits the use of any statement which suggests that a liquor is or resembles a sweetened liqueur unless it is a suitably flavoured compounded spirit which has been rendered sweet and viscous only by the addition of sucrose, dextrose or invert sugar and not by the use of any other ingredient. 'Vin de liqueur' is however allowed to describe a wine with a natural sugar content remaining after fermentation of grape juice to a minimum alcohol content of 14 per cent by volume. Recent changes in the Common Customs Tariff have resulted in 'vin de liqueur' being required to contain a minimum of 15 per cent alcohol by volume: we accept this change and *recommend* that Regulation 17(iii) be suitably amended. We consider that the reference in this Regulation to 'sucrose, dextrose or invert sugar' might be more suitably replaced by 'any sugar', sugar being defined as 'any carbohydrate sweetening matter'. We *recommend* accordingly.

154. *Use of the word 'champagne'.* Regulation 17(iv) prohibits the use of anything which suggests that cider and perry which has not undergone secondary fermentation is in any way connected with champagne. We understand that champagne will eventually be controlled by EEC wine

regulations and as such the 1970 Regulations would then no longer apply. Pending control by EEC regulations we however *recommend* that Regulation 17(iv) be deleted.

155. *Use of the word 'vintage'.* Regulation 17(vi) prohibits the use of the word 'vintage' or anything similar except in relation to brandy or to wine obtained by the fermentation in the district of its origin of the juice of freshly gathered grapes. For cider, however, 'vintage' may be used in or in conjunction with the expression 'made from vintage apples'. In paragraph 119 of our 1964 Report on Food Labelling we recommended that the word should not be used in relation to cider since its use in that context was misleading. 'Vintage' was originally used to mean a cider at least three years old or of an alcoholic strength in excess of 15 per cent proof. In recent times it has been used to mean a cider of superior quality, strength or taste, the term 'made from vintage apples' being used in this sense. We still consider that such a use is misleading, particularly since the term 'vintage apples' is so difficult to define. We therefore *recommend* that the use of the term 'vintage' in relation to cider as at present permitted by Regulation 17(vi) should no longer be allowed.

156. *Shandy and like products.* The labelling, advertising and alcoholic strength of shandies are controlled by Regulations 17(vii) to (x). All must have a minimum alcoholic strength of 1.5 per cent proof spirit. Products described as 'shandy' or similar must be a mixture of beer and lemonade: 'shandy gaff' or 'gingerbeer shandy' must be beer and gingerbeer: 'cider shandy' or 'cyder shandy' must be cider and lemonade: 'cider shandy gaff' or 'cyder shandy gaff' or 'cider and gingerbeer shandy' or 'cyder and gingerbeer shandy' must be cider and gingerbeer. Section 73 of the Alcoholic Liquor Duties Act 1979[40] is also relevant in that it controls the mis-labelling of goods as beer.

157. Paragraphs 109 to 111 of our 1966 Report on Claims and Misleading Descriptions set out the background to the then existing controls. Although the minimum alcoholic strength for shandy recommended in that Report was higher (1.7 per cent proof spirit) than the figure in the 1970 Labelling of Food Regulations we would not wish to see any changes in the existing requirements, which appear to be operating satisfactorily. We see no reason to prohibit the widespread sale of shandies in unlicensed premises, as might occur if the alcohol content were raised. We would however like to see the existing provisions simplified: as set out in Regulation 17(vii) to (x) they are complicated and difficult to understand. We *recommend* accordingly. We discussed the ending of the use of 'per cent proof spirit' and its replacement by 'per cent alcohol by volume' in relation to the declaration of alcohol content in paragraph 145 above. The minimum alcoholic strength for shandies which is prescribed in the Regulations in terms of 'per cent proof spirit' should similarly be changed. An appropriate figure to replace 1.5 per cent proof spirit

---

[40]The Alcoholic Liquor Duties Act 1979: C 4

would be 0.85 per cent alcohol by volume as referred to in paragraph 34(4) of our 1976 Report on Soft Drinks.

158. We discussed shandies and like products in paragraphs 52-54 of our 1976 Report on Soft Drinks, where we considered it unsatisfactory that many products of a type similar to shandy (such as lager and lime) did not have to comply with any minimum requirement for alcholic strength. We recommended that all such products labelled to suggest the presence of alcohol should comply with the minimum 1.5 per cent proof spirit requirement that currently applies to prepacked products labelled as shandies. We endorse this recommendation in this Report.

159. *Use of the term 'non-alcoholic'*. Regulation 17(xi) prohibits the use of the term 'non-alcoholic' in relation to any non-intoxicating liquor to qualify any name or word commonly associated with an intoxicating liquor. Descriptions such as 'non-alcoholic whisky' are therefore not allowed. 'Non-alcoholic wine' is however permitted to describe a product derived from unfermented grape juice intended exclusively for communion or sacramental use and which is described clearly as being exclusively for such use. We consider that these provisions are operating effectively and should be retained. Implementation of the EEC restrictions on the use of the word 'wine' (paragraph 152 above) will need to ensure that the use of 'non-alcoholic wine' to describe sacramental or communion wine can continue and we *recommend* accordingly.

160. *'Dealcoholised' wine*. We have been told that it is possible to remove the alcohol from wine by a process of evaporation. Other changes take place as the alcohol vapourises but a product is left at the end of the process which is described as 'dealcoholised' wine. We have been told that the end product has all the characteristics of wine except for the alcohol and if this is so the description above would seem to be appropriate. We would not wish legislation to stand in the way of the sale of this product provided it is suitably labelled. EEC wine regulations restricting the use of the word 'wine' will need to be examined in this respect and we *recommend* accordingly. However, before any steps are taken to permit its use, the labelling and compositional aspects will need to be examined to establish a suitably appropriate description. Where a particular type of wine has been used as a basis for this product, an appropriate designation of that type of wine should be included as a part of the description, which might take the form 'dealcoholised wine, made from 'X'', where 'X' is the appropriate designation of the complete wine from which the alcohol has been removed. We *recommend* that a declaration of alcoholic strength should be required on the labels of all these products: this will inform the consumer of any residual alcohol which may be present. Where alcohol is completely absent, we would expect the declaration to be in the form 'contains no alcohol'.

Tenderised meat (Regulation 18 and Schedule 5)

161. Meat to which proteolytic enzymes have been added will fall within our

recommended definition of 'meat product' in our forthcoming Report on Meat Products and the requirements of Regulation 18 and Schedule 5 to the 1970 Labelling of Food Regulations are considered in that Report.

Foods contact frozen with liquid freezant (Regulation 18A and Schedule 5)

162. This Regulation was introduced into the 1970 Labelling of Food Regulations by the Miscellaneous Additives in Food (Amendment) Regulations 1975[41]. These Amendment Regulations followed from recommendations by the Food Additives and Contaminants Committee[42] that dichlorodifluoromethane, a liquid freezant, should be added to the list of permitted miscellaneous additives in the 1974 Miscellaneous Additives in Food Regulations as amended. The consequent 1975 Miscellaneous Additives in Food (Amendment) Regulations added this substance to the list of permitted miscellaneous additives and at the same time introduced the new Regulation 18A of the 1970 Labelling of Food Regulations to deal with the labelling of foods frozen with dichlorodifluoromethane. Our advice was sought by the Food Additives and Contaminants Committee on the labelling controls necessary and these are reflected in Regulation 18A.

163. Regulation 18A requires that when a prepacked food sold by retail has been frozen with dichlorodifluoromethane, one of the following statements must be given on the label, in or in immediate proximity to the appropriate designation or common or usual name — 'contact frozen with permitted liquid freezant' or 'contact frozen with permitted dichlorodifluoromethane'. Paragraph 12A of Schedule 5 to the 1970 Labelling of Food Regulations (also introduced by the 1975 Miscellaneous Additives in Food (Amendment) Regulations) requires that the letters in the statement shall not be less than 2mm in height. When non-prepacked foods are so frozen and sold by retail, one of these statements must appear on a ticket on or in immediate proximity to the food so as to be clearly visible to an intending purchaser. In both instances 'permitted' is optional. When such frozen food is delivered for sale otherwise than by retail the purchaser must be notified at or before delivery that the food has been so frozen.

164. The labelling of foods frozen with dichlorodifluoromethane is controlled in this way because residues of the substance might remain in these foods following freezing. The residues present no hazard to health however and there is a statutory limit on the residue level permitted in fully thawed food. Because of the possibility of residues remaining we took the view that the consumer should be notified of the use of this contact freezant by means of a special declaration. Other freezants used, such as liquid nitrogen and solid carbon dioxide, do not leave an appreciable residue in the food.

---

[41]England and Wales SI 1975 No 1485
Scotland SI 1975 No 1596 (S227)
Northern Ireland SR & O (NI) 1975 No 275
[42]Food Additives and Contaminants Committee Supplementary Report on a Review of Liquid Freezants in Food:
FAC/REP/19: MAFF 1974

165.   Regulation 18A would appear to be operating satisfactorily and we *recommend* that it be retained. We are doubtful however as to the value to the consumer of a generic term such as 'liquid freezant' appearing on labels. The term could, but does not, also cover other liquid freezants and there is no similar requirement to declare the presence of these since no appreciable residue is left in the frozen food. If other contact refrigerants are likely to be permitted in the future, then a suitable general phrase might be permitted to cover these alternatives. Until such time, however, the use of dichlorodifluoromethane   should be identified specifically. Because the name is likely to mean little to the consumer we *recommend* that the declaration of contact freezant should take the form 'contact frozen with liquid freezant dichlorodifluoromethane'. 'Permitted' may precede 'liquid freezant'.

166.   The presence of dichlorodifluoromethane may also need to be declared in the list of ingredients. In these circumstances the generic term 'liquid freezant' will be sufficiently informative since it will already have been associated with the refrigerant used in the special declaration accompanying the appropriate designation. We *recommend* accordingly. This repeats the recommendation in paragraph 53 of our Report on Ingredient Listing.

167.   The EEC Food Labelling Directive contains no specific provisions for contact frozen food although such foods might be covered by Article 5(3) as discussed in paragraph 127 above. Even if not covered by Article 5(3), Regulation 18A can probably be retained under Article 4(2) which makes provision for the maintenance of existing national provisions applicable to specified foods.

Processed peas (Regulation 19)

168.   Regulation 19 requires that if the word 'peas' is used anywhere on a label or *in an advertisement* to describe any canned or frozen peas which have been dried or soaked prior to canning or freezing it must be preceded immediately by the word 'processed' in identical lettering. In a list of ingredients, however, 'dried peas' or 'soaked peas' may be substituted for 'processed peas'. Processed peas may not be described as 'fresh', 'garden' or 'green' or in any way which suggests that they have not been previously soaked or dried.

169.   We recognise that this Regulation might no longer be necessary by virtue of Article 5(3) of the EEC Food Labelling Directive as referred to in paragraph 127 above. We consider however that for these products there is a need for the retention of specific labelling requirements and therefore *recommend* that Regulation 19 be retained. In the context of providing greater information for the consumer we are doubtful whether the term 'processed peas' conveys much to the average consumer despite of its long established usage. In the absence of any suitable alternative term however we can only *recommend* its retention in future legislation. We note that canned or frozen peas which have been previously soaked or dried cannot be described as

'fresh', 'garden' or 'green'. We have seen this description applied to dried peas sold as 'Quick-dried garden peas' but we do not consider that this practice is consistent with the existing controls on canned and frozen peas. We therefore *recommend* that the descriptions 'fresh', 'garden' or 'green' should no longer be permitted to describe any peas which have been dried and it will be for manufacturers to find suitably attractive alternative descriptions. We appreciate the steps that have been taken to prepare some forms of dried peas which, after cooking, have a reasonable claim to be regarded as of high quality. Even so, it would be too difficult to frame a definition which would adequately differentiate them from other types of dried peas.

170. *Canned garden peas with sulphur dioxide added in place of colouring matter.* We were asked for our advice following comments from interested parties in response to a Food Additives and Contaminants Committee (FACC) Report[43] on the use of sulphur dioxide as an alternative to permitted colouring matter in canned garden peas. In that Report the FACC recommended that sulphur dioxide to a maximum level of 100 mg/kg should be permitted in canned garden peas to which no colouring matter had been added. The most commonly used method of canning peas in the UK at present involves the addition of permitted colours to restore the green colour lost when natural chlorophyll is destroyed during heat processing. The process which is discussed in the FACC Report obviates the need to add colour, since the natural colouring survives. This is achieved by creating a slightly alkaline product by the addition of sodium hydroxide and monosodium glutamate. Sulphur dioxide is however also required to offset the development of unattractive odours which may result from the increased alkalinity, but its use in canned garden peas is not permitted. The only preservative at present permitted in these products is nisin. The FACC therefore recommended in its Report that sulphur dioxide be permitted so that this alternative manufacturing process could be used. Sodium hydroxide is permitted in food by the 1974 Miscellaneous Additives in Food Regulations as amended. Monosodium glutamate is at present controlled only by the general provisions of the Food and Drugs Acts although in its Report on the Review of Flavour Modifiers[44] the FACC has now recommended that flavour modifiers be controlled by permitted list and that this should include monosodium glutamate.

171. Representations on the FACC Report suggested that peas canned by this new process should be subject to extra labelling requirements to enable consumers to distinguish readily between the new product and 'traditional' canned garden peas. The comments suggested either that the new process was sufficiently different to warrant a new designation or that the addition of monosodium glutamate should be made more apparent than a reference to it solely in a list of ingredients.

---

[43]Food Additives and Contaminants Committee Report on a Representation for the Use of Sulphur Dioxide as an Alternative to Permitted Colouring Matter in Canned Garden Peas: FAC/REP/23: MAFF 1977.

[44]Food Additives and Contaminants Committee Review of Remaining Classes of Food Additives Used as Ingredients in Food. Report on the Review of Flavour Modifiers: FAC/REP/28: HMSO 1978.

172. We have considered the above views very carefully in the light of existing circumstances of sale and labelling requirements. At present, although canned garden peas without added colouring matter are available on the UK market, we have been told that their sale is not substantial as consumers find the colour of such peas unattractive. The majority of canned peas therefore contain added colour, which will be declared in the list of ingredients together with the preservative nisin, if used. The alternative process will employ monosodium glutamate, sodium hydroxide and preservative (sulphur dioxide) which will have to be listed as ingredients. An interested consumer could therefore distinguish between the different products. We can therefore see no reason for further separate labelling requirements for canned garden peas with added sulphur dioxide, either in the form of a different appropriate designation or a special declaration of additives. The latter requirement would be discriminatory when declarations of additives in other products are generally only required in an ingredients list and we see no reason to treat additives differently in this respect from other ingredients. We *recommend* accordingly. We also considered the possibility that manufacturers producing canned garden peas by the new process would wish to draw the absence of colouring matter to the purchaser's attention (eg 'free from added colour'). Such a declaration could be misleading since a purchaser could infer from it a complete absence of additives. We therefore *recommend* that any such declarations on labels should be accompanied by an indication of all the additives present in immediate proximity to the appropriate designation.

Use of the words 'milk', 'butter' and 'cream' (Regulation 20)

173. *'Milk'*. Regulation 20 of the 1970 Labelling of Food Regulations restricts the use of the words 'milk', 'butter' and 'cream'. Regulation 20(1) requires that where the word 'milk' or anything similar is used on a label or in an advertisement as part of the name of a food or of an ingredient or constituent, the food must contain cow's milk with all the normal constituents. The word may however be used to describe milk other than whole cow's milk provided it is suitably qualified, eg goat's milk, skimmed milk, or is used in such a context as to indicate clearly that it does not refer to milk or any of its constituents or is used in accordance with other regulations made under the Food and Drugs Act 1955.

174. Regulation 20(1) follows recommendations in paragraph 160 of our 1964 Report on Food Labelling where the use of the word 'milk' was discussed in relation to biscuits. We consider that Regulation 20(1) fully reflects our recommendations. We have been told that it is working satisfactorily and that few difficulties have arisen in its operation and we therefore *recommend* that Regulation 20(1) be retained.

175. *'Butter'*. Regulation 20(2) restricts the use of the word 'butter' when used in the labelling and advertising of *sugar confectionery* and *chocolate confectionery*. Where 'butter' or anything similar is used in the name, description or designation to suggest that butter is present, the confectionery

63

or the part to which the word is applied must contain at least 4% by weight of milk fat. Although chocolate products are excluded from the definition of 'chocolate confectionery' in Regulation 2(1) and therefore Regulation 20(2) does not apply to these products, Regulation 6(ii) of the Cocoa and Chocolate Products Regulations 1976[45] contains a similar requirement for the fillings in filled chocolates. We *recommend* that all these provisions be retained.

176.   We discussed the use of the word 'butter' in the name of a product of which it is an ingredient, in paragraphs 91-94 of our 1966 Report on Claims and Misleading Descriptions. We accepted that it was not necessary for all the fat in sugar confectionery and chocolate products to be butterfat, provided they contained sufficient butter to characterise them and that the figure of 4% in a Ministry of Food Code of Practice (M.F.21/51) was appropriate in this respect. Flour confectionery and biscuits were considered more appropriate for control by a code of practice then being negotiated between the industry and the former Local Authorities' Joint Advisory Committee on Food Standards (LAJAC). The subject was further considered in paragraphs 120-122 of our 1974 Second Report on Bread and Flour[46] where we were of the view that a reference to 'butter' in the name of a cake should be allowed only if all the added fat was butterfat. We took this view since many consumers could be expected to know the composition of cakes as made at home and to be familiar with recipes which gave butter as the only fat. It was therefore likely that consumers would, in the absence of a full list of ingredients, think that the inclusion of 'butter' in the name of a product meant that all the fat was butter. With biscuits we considered that it was not essential for all the fat to be butterfat provided sufficient was present to characterise the product: we considered that to achieve this at least two-thirds of the fat should be butterfat. Consumers would not be as familiar with the composition of biscuits as with cakes and would not necessarily think that all the fat was butter if the name of a biscuit referred to butter eg *'petit beurre'*. We were also of the view that cakes which contained only a proportion of butter should be permitted to carry sub-designations such as 'containing butter' only if butter constituted a minimum of 5% of the cake crumb. We recommended that if a code of practice had not been agreed by the time new bread and flour regulations came to be drafted, these regulations should include appropriate legal requirements.

177.   The code of practice referred to above still remains to be agreed and new bread and flour regulations arising from the recommendations in our 1974 Report have yet to be made. We therefore consider that the use of the word 'butter' in flour confectionery and biscuits should no longer remain outside specific statutory control and we so *recommend*. We have examined the controls which will be necessary, particularly since these foods will no longer be exempt from an ingredient declaration. Where a product contains butter and other fats, manufacturers will probably choose to declare the butter

---

[45]England and Wales SI 1976 No 541
   Scotland SI 1976 No 914 (S 78)
   Northern Ireland SR(NI) 1976 No 183.
[46]Food Standards Committee Second Report on Bread and Flour: FSC/REP/61: HMSO 1974.

specifically and, for the other fats, may make use of an appropriate generic term such as 'vegetable fat' (as recommended in paragraph 52 of our Report on Ingredient Listing). From their relative positions in the ingredients list a consumer will be able to tell which of the two has been used in the greater quantity but this may not coincide with the consumer's own understanding of the composition of the product, particularly if the presence of 'butter' is emphasised in the name. Because different fats are listed in the ingredients declaration, it does not in our view detract from the principle that where the presence of butter is emphasised by the use of the word in the name of a food, sufficient should be present *at least* to characterise the food. With cakes a consumer will expect all the fat to be butter. We therefore *recommend* that the existing controls in Regulation 20(2) of the 1970 Labelling of Food Regulations be extended in any future legislation to include the use of the word 'butter' in flour confectionery and biscuits as set out in paragraph 176 above. Where sub-designations such as 'contains butter' are applied in accordance with paragraph 176, these will also fall to be controlled by Article 7 of the EEC Food Labelling Directive as discussed in paragraphs 51 to 54 above so that the minimum percentage of butter present will need to be declared.

178.   In paragraph 120 of our 1974 Second Report on Bread and Flour we referred to Regulation 6(6) of the 1970 Labelling of Food Regulations which would apply to sub-designations such as 'containing butter' and which would require a full list of ingredients to be given although in the absence of the sub-designation no list would be required. In the context of full ingredient declarations being required for all but a very small proportion of prepacked foods, Regulation 6(6) will cease to apply to a number of foods such as cakes and biscuits but we have nonetheless recommended its retention in paragraph 75 above.

179.   *'Cream'*. Regulation 20(2) contains controls on the use of the word 'cream' similar to those outlined above for butter. *Sugar confectionery* and *chocolate confectionery* must contain at least 4% by weight of milk fat if the word 'cream' or anything similar is used in the name on a label or in an advertisement. Chocolate products are excluded from the definition of 'chocolate confectionery' in Regulation 2(1) and Regulation 20(2) of the 1970 Labelling Regulations therefore does not apply to these (as with the use of the word 'butter' in paragraph 175 above). Regulation 6(ii) of the 1976 Cocoa and Chocolate Products Regulations however requires a minimum of 4% milk fat in the filling of filled chocolate before the word 'cream' may be used in the name on a label or in an advertisement. 'Cream chocolate' listed in Schedule 1 to those Regulations must contain a minimum of 7% milk fat.

180.   The use of the word 'cream' in relation to *all* foods is also controlled by Regulation 8 of the Cream Regulations 1970, as amended[47]. 'Cream' or

---

[47]England and Wales SI 1970 No 752 as amended by SI 1975 No 1486
Scotland SI 1970 No 1191 (S98) as amended by SI 1975 No 1597 (S228)
Northern Ireland SR & O 1970 No 194 as amended by SR & O 1976 No 15

anything similar, unless used in accordance with specific provisions of the Act or regulations, may only be used on labels or tickets or in advertisements if:

(a)   the food is cream as defined; or

(b)   the word is used in such a context as to indicate clearly that the substance to which it refers is an ingredient of the food and is cream as defined; or

(c)   the word is used in such a context as to indicate clearly that the food is not, and does not contain, cream.

Nothing in the Regulations prohibits the use of 'creamed' in relation to food which is not butter, milk, cream, condensed, dried or evaporated milk, cheese, skimmed milk or skimmed milk with non-milk fat.

181.   All these statutory controls stem from recommendations made in paragraphs 95 and 96 of our 1966 Report on Claims and Misleading Descriptions. We were of the opinion that the word 'cream' could be used where long-established usage can be established, such as salad cream and confectionery cream, and also where the context made absolutely clear that the use of the word did not imply the presence of butterfat. Otherwise, the use of the word 'cream', imitations such as 'kreme', 'kreem' and 'creme' and the word 'creamy' should be governed by the general principle expressed in paragraph 80 of our 1966 Report that when a name or description incorporated the name of a food, that food should customarily be present in significant quantity. The amount present would vary in different circumstances but the main criterion should not necessarily be what is current common commercial practice. At the same time we did not consider it objectionable to use the word 'creamed' for products, not wholly or mainly dairy products, which had been subjected to a process of air absorption or emulsification to achieve plasticity of texture or, being oil or fat, had been subject to the mechanical action of mixing with water to form a creamy emulsion. This recommendation did not apply to soups which are dealt with in paragraphs 33-35 of our 1968 Report on Soups, where a minimum butterfat content was recommended for soups described as 'cream of . . . .' or 'cream' and a minimum fat content was recommended for soups described as 'creamed'.

182.   We consider that the existing controls in the 1970 Labelling of Food Regulations and the 1970 Cream Regulations deal adequately with the use of the word 'cream': cases of long-established usage are protected and other references are required to be clear to consumers. In the most important instances (sugar confectionery, chocolate confectionery and chocolate products) where the characterising proportion of cream present in a food that uses the word 'cream' in the name needs to be defined, the appropriate levels have been set by Regulation 20(2) of the 1970 Labelling of Food Regulations and Regulation 6(ii) of the 1976 Cocoa and Chocolate Products Regulations. All other instances fall to be controlled by the general provisions of Regulation 8 of the 1970 Cream Regulations and the Food and Drugs Acts. We regret that

controls on 'cream' soups have not been included in legislation in accordance with the recommendation in paragraph 38 of our 1968 Report on Soups but we appreciate that this control is more appropriate to compositional rather than labelling regulations. We therefore *recommend* that the existing requirements of Regulation 20(2) be retained.

183.   Section 47 of the 1955 Food and Drugs Act also controls the use of the word 'cream', but in relation to reconstituted and artificial products. Any substance resembling cream but which is not cream, or any food containing such a substance, may not be sold under a description which includes the word 'cream'. The sale of reconstituted or artificial cream is however permitted provided these are identified as such and the sale of any other similar substance is also permitted provided it is not sold for use as cream or as a substitute for it. Reconstituted cream is defined as a substance resembling cream and containing no ingredient not derived from milk, except water or other ingredients lawfully permitted to be used in cream. Imitation cream is defined as a substance resembling cream which is produced by emulsifying edible oils or fats with water, either by themselves or with other non-prohibited substances.

184.   We have examined Section 47 of the Food and Drugs Act 1955 in the light of the other existing controls of the 1970 Labelling of Food Regulations, the 1976 Cocoa and Chocolate Products Regulations, the 1970 Cream Regulations and Sections 2 and 6 of the Act itself. We consider that these provisions taken together provide sufficient protection for consumers against the sale of food which looks like, but is not, cream. We have been told that sales of reconstituted cream are now insignificant if not non-existent because of the much greater use of refrigeration and we believe that if a definition of imitation cream serves a useful purpose it should be in regulations and not in the Act. We *recommend* therefore that consideration be given to the deletion of Section 47 of the Food and Drugs Act 1955 (and the equivalent provisions of the Scottish and Northern Ireland Acts) and the inclusion of a similar provision to control imitation cream in regulations. This could be done as part of the review of the Acts which is currently being undertaken by Government Departments.

185.   The controls exercised by Regulation 20 may be more appropriate for specific compositional regulations and this will need to be considered when proposals for new labelling regulations are being discussed. We *recommend* accordingly.

Specific requirements for other foods

186.   A number of compositional regulations and also our Reports concerned with particular commodities or groups of commodities include provisions or recommended provisions concerning labelling. These provisions are, in most instances, designed to meet specific needs for the particular foods. In our Reports we have always had regard for the relation of such specific provisions

to the 1970 Labelling of Food Regulations and to the principles in our 1964 Labelling and 1966 Claims Reports. In recent years we have also taken into account many of the views which have been prompted by the present Labelling Review and by the EEC Food Labelling Directive. There would be no merit in detailing all the labelling references for these various foods, but, where they have significance in our current review, they are referred to in the appropriate section of this Report.

V MANNER OF MARKING

Regulation 28(1) and Schedule 5

187.   Regulation 28(1) of the 1970 Labelling of Food Regulations requires that any information to be given on food labels in accordance with the Regulations must comply with the manner of marking provisions of Schedule 5. The Schedule contains general requirements applicable to all foods covered by the Regulations and specific requirements applicable to certain information or particular foods as follows.

188.   *General requirements applicable to all information required by the 1970 Labelling of Food Regulations.* All the information required by the 1970 Labelling of Food Regulations must be given in accordance with paragraphs 1 to 4 of Schedule 5 and hence must be:

   (a)   clear and legible;

   (b)   in a conspicuous position on the label or on a ticket on or in immediate proximity to the food so as to be readily discernible and easily read by an intending purchaser or consumer under normal conditions of purchase or use;

   (c)   not interrupted by other written or pictorial matter so as to mislead as to the nature of the food;

   (d)   not in any way hidden or obscured or reduced in conspicuousness by any other matter on the label.

In addition, the letters in each word must be in characters of uniform colour and size (disregarding any inconsiderable variation) and on a contrasting ground. Initial letters of words may be taller than any other letter in the word and the letters of any preposition, conjunction or participle may be shorter than the letters in any other word.

189.   *The appropriate designation or common or usual name.* Paragraph 5 of Schedule 5 requires that any appropriate designation or common or usual name must be:

   (a)   in characters of a minimum specified size related to the greatest dimension of the container (as defined in Regulation 2(1)) and minimum sizes of letters are specified in paragraph 13 of Schedule 5 as follows (these minima do not apply to prepositions, conjunctions or participles in the designation or name):

Greatest dimension of container	Minimum height of letters in the appropriate designation or common or usual name
Not exceeding 12 cm	2 mm
Exceeding 12 cm but not exceeding 30 cm	3 mm
Exceeding 30 cm but not exceeding 45 cm	6 mm
Exceeding 45 cm	8 mm

and

(b) more prominent than any other material required by the Regulations and 'so prominent in height, visual emphasis and position on the label as to be conspicuous by comparison with any other matter (whether pictorial or not) on the same or any other label on the container, under normal conditions of purchase'.

The height of the letters in any word in the appropriate designation or common or usual name must not be calculated by any undue or insufficient prominence to mislead as to the nature, substance or quality of the food; and the height of the letters in a word describing a minor ingredient should not give undue prominence to that ingredient when the designation or name is taken as a whole. Foods which had already been labelled in accordance with the Labelling of Food Regulations 1967 in anticipation of those Regulations coming into force (see paragraph 3 above) are provided for in paragraph 5(4) of Schedule 5.

190.   *The ingredients list.* Paragraph 6 of Schedule 5 sets out the manner of marking requirements for the ingredients list and the heading to the list, which must be:

(a) in immediate proximity to the appropriate designation or common or usual name, *or*

(b) simultaneously visible with the appropriate designation or common or usual name under normal conditions of purchase or use, *or*

(c) within a surrounding line or on a panel which is clearly distinguished in colour from the adjacent parts of the label. No other information may appear within the surrounding line or on the panel other than information required by legislation.

The minimum sizes of letters to be used (other than in a preposition, conjunction or participle), are related to the greater dimension of the container and are set out in paragraph 13 of Schedule 5 as follows:

Greatest dimension of container	Minimum height of letters in the ingredients list
Not exceeding 12 cm	1 mm
Exceeding 12 cm but not exceeding 30 cm	1.5 mm
Exceeding 30 cm but not exceeding 45 cm	3 mm
Exceeding 45 cm	4 mm

The word or words heading or preceding the ingredients list may be taller than the words in the list.

191. *Bottles containing soft drinks.* Paragraph 7 of Schedule 5 provides that certain containers of soft drinks may bear the appropriate designation or common or usual name and the ingredients list on the cork, stopper or cap, rather than on the label. These containers are those which carry no words other than those on the cork, stopper or cap or those which are embossed or fired on the container and where those words do not contravene any provisions of the Regulations. The ingredients list so marked does not have to be in immediate proximity to or simultaneously visible with the appropriate designation or common or usual name or within a surrounding line or on a panel provided the words in the appropriate designation or common or usual name are not less than 1 mm in height.

192. *Other requirements.* Paragraphs 8 to 12A of Schedule 5 set out requirements in relation to the manner of marking of prepacked foods exempt from ingredient listing, non-prepacked foods, acetic acid, intoxicating liquor, tenderized meat and food contact frozen with liquid freezant. Requirements for these are referred to in paragraphs 72, 89, 124, 143, 161 and 163 respectively of this report.

Effects of the EEC Food Labelling Directive

193. Detailed manner of marking requirements such as those in Schedule 5 to the 1970 Labelling of Food Regulations are not contained in the EEC Food Labelling Directive. We were informed that in discussions in Brussels on the Directive, the United Kingdom argued strongly for the inclusion of such detailed provisions but the concept of detailed control of the manner in which information is presented on the label was unacceptable to other Member States. The resultant manner of marking requirements in the Directive are consequently set out only in very general terms.

194. Manner of marking is covered by Articles 11 and 14 of the Directive.

Article 11.2 specifies that information required by the Directive or Community or national provisions relating to specified foods must be 'easy to understand and marked in a conspicuous place in such a way as to be easily visible, clearly legible and indelible'. The information must not 'in any way be hidden, obscured or interrupted by other written or pictorial matter'. The name of the food, the net quantity and the date mark must appear 'in the same field of vision': this requirement can be extended to other Community or national provisions applicable to specified foods. 'Glass bottles intended for re-use' with indelible markings are exempt from this requirement for a period of ten years following notification of the Directive. With packaging or containers where the largest surface area is less than 10cm^2, Member States are free to require only the name, net quantity and datemark on the label. Member States are also free to require only certain information for re-usable bottles for milk and milk products and to exempt these from the 'same field of vision' requirement. Under Article 14, Member States must refrain from laying down requirements for the manner of marking which are more detailed than those in Article 11.

195. The effects of Articles 11 and 14 of the Directive are such that any future UK requirements relating to manner of marking can only be as detailed as is justified by the wording in the Directive. Detailed and specific requirements such as those in Schedule 5 to the 1970 Labelling of Food Regulations will therefore no longer be allowed. Such a move to general rather than specific manner of marking requirements is in our view a retrograde step and to be deprecated. Although the provisions of Schedule 5 have presented certain difficulties in enforcement, they are generally effective and help to ensure that information of use to the consumer is presented on labels clearly and conspicuously. They have also made labelling easier for the manufacturer, who has had a precise set of rules with which to comply rather than general guidance. Removal of the detailed controls in Schedule 5 may well entail a reversion to the difficulties which were encountered with the use of the general controls in the Labelling of Food Order 1953, which we discussed in paragraphs 42 to 44 of our 1964 Report on Food Labelling. In that Report we considered that the development of prepacking and self-service retailing had led to a 'greater need for clearly legible and conspicuous statutory declarations' for the benefit of both consumers and traders. We said that there was a need for much greater emphasis to be placed on well-designed labels which readily informed the consumer of the nature of the food: this should be the prime objective of regulations. In discussing the provisions of the Labelling of Food Order 1953 which required information to be 'clearly legible' and to 'appear conspicuously and in a prominent position on the label', we were of the view that these were 'too imprecise always to achieve the minimum desirable presentation' and that 'The overriding consideration is the inherent right of the prospective consumer, with reasonable scrutiny of a prepacked food, readily to see and read the information which the law requires to be put on the label'. This must remain the overriding consideration today. With general requirements such as those of the Labelling of Food Order 1953 we said that 'The prominence and conspicuousness of the statutory

declarations are much more open to argument and produce more evidence of fault and we are informed that an appreciable amount of argument occurs on this subject between enforcing authorities and manufacturers'. For these reasons we concluded that the then existing general requirements 'should be supplemented by specific directions'. We remain of this view.

196.   Recognizing that Schedule 5 to the 1970 Labelling of Food Regulations will no longer continue in its existing form once the EEC Food Labelling Directive is implemented, we have examined Articles 11 and 14 of the Directive to ascertain the extent to which any of the provisions of Schedule 5 may be retained in future UK food labelling law. Our conclusions are set out below.

197.   *General requirements.* It would appear that most of the general requirements of paragraph 1 of Schedule 5 as set out in paragraph 188 above are covered by Article 11.2 which requires that particulars must be 'easy to understand and marked in a conspicuous place in such a way as to be easily visible, clearly legible and indelible'. The provisions of paragraph 1(d) of Schedule 5 requiring that information should not be '. . . . reduced in conspicuousness . . .' are not specifically covered by the wording in the Directive, although this is arguably unnecessary in view of the requirement in the Directive for information to be '. . . . in a conspicuous place . . . .'. We understand, however, that the whole of paragraph 1 of Schedule 5 has been incorporated in UK legislation implementing other EEC directives which contain general provisions similar to those in the Food Labelling Directive. We therefore *recommend* that the general requirement of paragraph 1 of Schedule 5, relating to the manner of marking of all the information required by the 1970 Labelling of Food Regulations, should be incorporated in any future labelling legislation.

198.   *The appropriate designation.* We consider that on any food label, the most important single item of information must be the *appropriate designation* as defined in paragraph 42. Without it, the consumer has no way of discovering the 'true nature' of the food. Because of its unique importance, there should be special manner of marking requirements for its presentation on labels. To help ensure adequate enforcement, any such requirements should be clear and specific. The reference in Article 11.3(a) of the Directive to the name of the food being 'in the same field of vision' as the net quantity and the date mark is not in our view sufficient to ensure that the *appropriate designation* will be sufficiently prominent. We said in paragraph 50 of our 1964 Report on Labelling that 'the test for a satisfactory declaration must be that the reasonably attentive and enquiring but busy customer can not only see the designation, but read it'. The requirements of the Directive do not meet this test. There would however appear to be no possibility of including in future labelling legislation valuable provisions which would meet our test such as those in paragraph 5(2) of Schedule 5 to the 1970 Labelling of Food Regulations, which require the appropriate designation or common or usual name to be '. . . . . . conspicuous by comparison with any other matter . . . . . .' on the label. We consider that the provisions of Article 11.2 and 11.3(a) of the

EEC Food Labelling Directive are inadequate in relation to this most important piece of information and we can only repeat our view that more detailed requirements are necessary to ensure that the information of greatest use to the consumer is presented on labels with sufficient prominence. We have been told that the provisions of Article 14, which prevents Member States from laying down more specific requirements than those in Article 11, will also apply to individual commodity regulations. There would seem therefore to be no opportunity available in the immediate future to require manner of marking requirements more detailed than those of Article 11, even where a particular commodity might warrant special labelling. This must indeed be a retrograde step for the consumer.

199.   *The list of ingredients.* The requirements of paragraph 6(1) of Schedule 5 to the 1970 Labelling of Food Regulations (paragraph 190 above) help to ensure that the ingredients list may always be readily identified on labels: this is particularly important since, without detailed controls, some manufacturers might place the list of ingredients away from the main information on the label and hence either in an obscure position or overshadowed by other matter on the label. Although there are no specific manner of marking requirements in Article 11 of the Directive, the list of ingredients must, like all other information, be '. . . . . in a conspicuous place . . . . .' and '. . . . . easily visible, clearly legible . . . .' Because of the tendency not to display the list of ingredients in a prominent position on the label, it is arguable that for it to meet the requirements of the Directive it will need to be clearly separate from the rest of the label and thus will need to be within a surrounding line or on a panel clearly distinguished from the rest of the label as in the 1970 Regulations. We therefore *recommend* that, if legally possible under the terms of Article 11 of the EEC Food Labelling Directive, future labelling legislation should require that the list of ingredients appear on labels within a surrounding line to distinguish it clearly from other information on the label and for it to be readily identified by the consumer.

200.   *Minimum size of type.* There are no provisions in the Directive requiring a minimum size of type for the information to be given on labels. We consider that a minimum size of type is required in some instances to avoid different interpretations of what may be 'clearly legible' etc. Without such minimum type sizes, the general requirement which will have to be incorporated in future labelling legislation will need to be drafted in as precise a manner as possible to avoid the possibility of any ambiguity of interpretation.

201.   *Code of practice.* Although the implementation of the Directive will mean the end of the many detailed manner of marking provisions in regulations, we would like to see their retention in a code of practice if this is permissible under the provisions of the Directive. This could provide sensible and welcome guidance to both manufacturers and enforcement officers. If Ministers had the power to introduce codes under the Food and Drugs Acts this would be the obvious place for such a code; since this is not the case however, we *recommend* that the local Authorities Co-ordinating Body on

Trading Standards (LACOTS) and the food industry do all that is possible to ensure that these detailed yet sensible and undoubtedly useful rules remain available and in use for the benefit of all concerned.

202. *Small containers.* We have already discussed the small container exemption in Article 11.4(a) of the Directive in relation to ingredient listing in paragraph 46 of our Report on Ingredient Listing (paragraphs 74 and 86 above refer). We repeat our view expressed there, that only where a minimum type size is set for the statutory information need there be any exemption for small containers. Where no such minimum type size is specified, as in the Directive, an exemption is not justified.

203. *Bottles containing soft drinks.* Paragraph 194 above refers to the provisions of Article 11.3(b) relating to glass bottles with indelible markings intended for re-use. We *recommend* that these provisions be examined to establish the extent to which the provisions of paragraph 7 of Schedule 5 to the 1970 Labelling of Food Regulations relating to bottles containing soft drinks (referred to in paragraph 191 above) may be incorporated in future labelling legislation.

Food prepacked in more than one container (Regulation 28(2))

204. Regulation 28(2) requires that if a food is prepacked in more than one container, information required by the Regulations must be on a label or attached to the outermost container or 'readily discernible and easily read' through that outermost container. This sensible requirement should be retained in future labelling legislation and we *recommend* accordingly. This requirement does not seem to conflict with any provisions of the EEC Food Labelling Directive.

Present requirements

205.   Whenever fish is sold by retail, whether prepacked or non-prepacked, it must *always* be identified. Appropriate designations·for certain species of fish are set out in Schedule 1 to the 1970 Labelling of Food Regulations as amended in 1972, 1976 and 1978: fish of species other than those listed in the Schedule must be described by an appropriate designation or common or usual name. The names listed in the Schedule (as referred to in paragraph 46) are appropriate designations by virtue of Regulation 3(5) of the 1970 Regulations, which also prohibits the application of any of these names, whether modified or not, to fish of a species different from that listed. Proviso (a) to Regulation 3(5) allows the qualification of the appropriate designation by the inclusion of a descriptive word or words to make it more specific. Proviso (b) allows the use of traditional names for fish which have been subjected to smoking or any similar process.

206.   Non-prepacked fish, by virtue of Regulation 9(1) and Part I of Schedule 3, must be ticketed with the appropriate designation specified in Schedule 1: if not a listed species, an appropriate designation or common or usual name must be given. As already discussed in paragraph 89, where any non-prepacked fish is sold for immediate consumption at or near the place of sale, or sold without having been previously exposed for sale, it is sufficient for the purchaser to be notified of these particulars at or before delivery (Regulations 9(3) and (4)).

207.   When fish is used as an ingredient of a fish product it may be designated as 'fish' in the ingredients list by virtue of Regulation 6(1) and Part I of Schedule 2. 'Fish product' is not defined although 'fish' is defined in Regulation 2(1) as including edible molluscs and crustacea. We have already recommended in paragraph 52 of our Report on Ingredient Listing at Appendix 2 that the generic terms 'fish' and 'other fish' be made available in future legislation for use in ingredient lists, provided that where 'fish' is used, the name and presentation of the food does not refer to any species of fish and that 'other fish' refers to kinds of fish not included in the appropriate designation.

Background

208.   The requirements of the 1970 Labelling of Food Regulations are based on recommendations made in paragraphs 153 to 156 and Appendix C of our 1964 Report on Food Labelling. At the time of that Report fish names were controlled only by the general provisions of the Food and Drugs Acts: a Ministry of Food Code of Practice (CP2) however designated the species of fish to be sold under names such as herring and pilchard. The Code of Practice also contained guidance about the qualification of names and the labelling of fish pastes. There was also in existence a list of recommended names for the

retail sale of fresh or frozen fish which had been issued by the White Fish Authority in January 1959, following representations to Ministers, and which indicated what constituted good practice. The list had been prepared in consultation with local authority associations and the fish trade.

209. At the time of our 1964 Report on Food Labelling it was suggested that '. . . . there is probably more confusion about the proper nomenclature of fish than about that of any other simple uncompounded food . . . .'. We considered that a list of prescribed names would be of value in helping to prevent 'passing off' and '. . . . in reducing the present confusion caused by the use of alternative names, some of which are misleading . . . .' . A tentative list of names for fresh and prepacked fish was set out at Appendix C to the 1964 Report.

Effects of the present law

210. The present law controlling fish names requires the name in Schedule 1 of the 1970 Labelling of Food Regulations, as amended, to be given for the appropriate species whenever it is sold by retail: there is no choice of name since the name in Schedule 1 is regarded for the purposes of the 1970 Regulations as *the* appropriate designation. Fish of a species not listed in Schedule 1 may be called by any suitable name provided it is not the same as, or a modification of, any of the names in the Schedule. The choice of a suitable name will of course remain subject to the general provisions of the Food and Drugs Acts and the 1970 Labelling of Food Regulations ie it must be described by an appropriate designation or common or usual name.

211. The requirements of the 1970 Labelling of Food Regulations would seem to be operating satisfactorily and a great deal has been achieved in helping to prevent 'passing off' of inferior species. But the operation of the Regulation has led to some difficulties, the more important of which are examined below. The recommendations which follow should help to overcome these difficulties.

212. *Names to be applied.* The name applied to a particular species of fish will often vary from country to country. *Glyptocephalus cynoglossus* (L.) for instance, sold as 'witch' in the United Kingdom, is known as 'grey plaice' ('plie grise') in France, 'gray sole' in the USA and 'grey flounder' elsewhere. Similarly 'roughback' *(Hippoglossoides platessoides* (Fabr.)) is known elsewhere as 'American plaice'. The requirements of the 1970 Labelling of Food Regulations prevent the use in England and Wales of names accepted in other countries for species for which a different name is already laid down in the Schedule. The Schedule in effect protects the 'quality' names of fish and prevents the application of these names, even when qualified, to species which might be regarded as of inferior quality. It is, for instance, often said that if the names 'plaice' and 'sole' were allowed to be qualified they would be used for other species such as 'dab', 'roughback', 'witch' and 'megrim', which are generally regarded as possessing less attractive eating characteristics. We have been told that the 'passing off' of flatfish other than *Solea solea* for 'sole' still

takes place and a number of prosecutions based on the 1970 Labelling of Food Regulations have been instituted. It should be noted that enforcement has been greatly aided by the development of effective analytical techniques for species determination. The degree of protection afforded by the 1970 Regulations needs to be maintained and we *recommend* that the existing system of control should therefore continue. We have been told that this will be permitted under the terms of the EEC Food Labelling Directive.

213.　The existing controls on the use of fish names do not prevent the addition of new names to the list in Schedule 1 (even if these qualify one already in use), provided a suitable case can be presented to Ministers. This may become increasingly necessary if and when changing fishing patterns result in less familiar species being available to the consumer. If no suitable name already exists, there may be a wish to indicate to the consumer the particular eating characteristics by the use of a name, suitably qualified, which has previously been applied to a different species of fish which is well known to the consumer for those particular characteristics. Where this is not misleading, appropriate amendments can be made to the Schedule: recent examples of such additions are 'blue whiting' *(Micromesistius poutassou)* and 'Alaska pollack' *(Theragra chalcogrammus),* both added to the Schedule by the 1976 Labelling of Food (Amendment) Regulations. It has been argued that amendment of the 1970 Regulations in this way is a cumbersome procedure to follow and takes a long time to put into effect. Because of the need to protect against the use of misleading names, however, it is necessary for any requests for additions or changes to the Schedule to be examined very carefully and for the views of all interested parties to be sought and considered in some detail. This will inevitably take time but in the circumstances we do not consider that this length of time adversely affects any particular interest. In any system which attempts to prevent the 'passing off' of inferior species of fish, whether this is in legislation or, as has been suggested, in a code of practice, it would seem to be unavoidable that changes to that system will take time to effect.

214.　A further criticism of the 1970 Regulations which has been made is that it cannot quickly reflect changes in the scientific classification of fish. These changes arise from revisions in fish nomenclature which occur as knowledge in this field increases. We consider, however, that where such need arises, suitable amendments can be made to the 1970 Regulations or to any regulations implementing the EEC Food Labelling Directive and we doubt whether the length of time involved will be in any way prejudicial to the interests of consumers, those who sell fish, or manufacturers.

215.　*Fish species or fish product.* Part I of Schedule 2 to the 1970 Labelling of Food Regulations allows fish which is an ingredient of a fish product to be described in the ingredients list as 'fish' and there is no requirement for the particular species to be identified. This could be held to imply that there is no specific requirement to identify the fish in the name of the fish product and that such product needs therefore be labelled only with an appropriate designation meeting the definition in Regulation 3(1) if no common or usual name such as 'fish cake' is available.

216.   Although the inclusion in legislation of a definition of fish product has been suggested, we do not consider that the existing provisions require any change and we *recommend* accordingly. We have been told that no problems in practice have arisen in distinguishing between fish sold as fish products and those sold as particular species. Although there may be difficulties in some particular areas, any attempt to specify a precise dividing line might well produce more problems than it solved. The need to refer in the appropriate designation to the particular species of fish used in a fish product will depend upon the nature of the product and the need for the appropriate designation to meet the definition in Regulation 3(1) in relation to indicating the 'true nature' of the food. In some circumstances this would seem to entail a reference to the species but in other circumstances, eg fish finger, fish pie, the need to do so seems more doubtful and in our view can be left to the choice of the manufacturer. We would not wish to see this measure of flexibility removed from the existing requirements. It will enable manufacturers to vary the fish ingredient in their products according to supply without the need to amend the appropriate designation, but only where this is not to the prejudice of the purchaser. We would not, however, wish this to be permitted where a manufacturer is, for instance, selling fillets or a particular cut of fish but wishes to avoid using species names for his product by using a description such as 'flat-fish fillets' or 'white fish steaks'. He might claim that there is a need to use such a description so that the species sold may be varied according to supply without the need to change the product name. Consumer choice of these products is based on the eating characteristics of the species of fish. To inform that it is being sold as a fillet or steak is important, if the shape is not clearly visible, but only in relation to the method of preparation and cooking. The present requirements of the 1970 Labelling of Food Regulations provide that an indication of the species must be given and the use of general descriptions is not provided for. Future legislation should maintain this situation and we *recommend* accordingly.

General principles of control for fish sold as such

217.   Having examined the major difficulties presented by the existing requirements of the 1970 Labelling of Food Regulations we have concluded that the present Schedule works satisfactorily and protects consumers whilst at the same time providing guidance for the food trade. The 1970 Regulations do not prevent the sale of fish of a species not listed in the Schedule, provided it is sold under an appropriate and not misleading name. Any major changes to the existing system would need to be an improvement on the protection already afforded and it has not been demonstrated to us that any alternative system could provide such improvement.

218.   To guide our detailed examination of Schedule 1 to the 1970 Labelling of Food Regulations, we considered the following principles:

    (a)   the *appropriate designation* as defined in paragraph 42 for fish should as now, always be given whether prepacked or non-prepacked when sold by retail;

(b)   the Schedule should be retained at about its present length.'Exotic' species of fish of which little is sold in the UK need not however be included, provided the principal 'quality' names are sufficiently protected;

(c)   where the use of alternative names for the same species of fish might be confusing, such names should be eliminated. The use of alternatives, even where not confusing, should be minimised. When an alternative name is acceptable, this may be used, but in most cases it is retained only in brackets after the 'main' name eg monkfish (angler). *The use of names in brackets will need to be reconsidered when the Schedule is next reviewed but it is our intention that their use will eventually be discontinued;*

(d)   following changes in the nomenclature of pilchards introduced by the 1978 Labelling of Food (Amendment) Regulations (which will in future require the name 'Pacific pilchard' to be used in place of the existing 'Californian pilchard', 'Chilean pilchard' and 'Japanese pilchard' and also 'South Atlantic pilchard' to be used in place of 'South African pilchard') further use of names referring to a specific country of origin should *where possible,* be avoided: it is more logical (and usually more correct) to refer instead to the principal waters in which the fish are caught. Country names could be confusing since they often bear no relation to the country of canning or the nationality of the fishing vessels. Any declaration of origin would best be left to the provisions of the Trade Descriptions Acts of 1968 and 1972 or to any legislation implementing the EEC Food Labelling Directive; in a few instances (Cape hake, Canary sole, Chinook salmon, Portuguese oyster) the names are so long established (and unambiguous) that they may be retained without causing confusion;

(e)   undefined terms such as 'large' and 'small', which are currently used for instance in the definitions of 'shrimps' and 'prawns', should be avoided where possible. Quantitative boundaries in terms of a size parameter provide a more satisfactory basis for distinguishing the names to be used;

(f)   authors' names should be retained as part of the Latin name as at present to avoid confusion;

(g)   there is no need to differentiate by means of a separate list between fish species sold fresh and those sold canned; and

(h)   traditional names for fish which have been smoked or subjected to a similar process should continue to be permitted.

219.   Using these principles, we have examined the existing Schedule of fish names with a view to ascertaining any necessary changes. In doing so we received much helpful advice from the British Museum (Natural History),

Torry Research Station and the Ministry of Agriculture, Fisheries and Food's Fisheries II Division. We discuss below our views in relation to certain of the more important species and the reasons for our choice of name. The application of the principles in paragraph 218 has been attempted as consistently as possible.

Sea fish

220.   *Black halibut*. We consider that this is a more appropriate name than the presently required 'Greenland halibut' or 'mock halibut' for fish of the species *Reinhardtius hippoglossoides* (Walbaum). 'Greenland halibut' should continue to be allowed but only as an additional name in brackets (see paragraph 218(c) above) after 'black halibut'. Its use would thus eventually be discontinued. 'Mock halibut' should be deleted from the Schedule since the use of such a 'negative' name could be confusing. We *recommend* accordingly.

221.   *Catfish*. At present, all fish of the species *Anarhichas* must be described as 'rockfish'. We consider that 'catfish' is a more appropriate and more widely understood name. 'Rockfish' may however accompany the name but in brackets. We *recommend* accordingly.

222.   *Hake*. A separate appropriate designation 'Cape hake' should be required for the species *Merluccius capensis* (Castelnau) and *Merluccius paradoxus* (Franca) since these fish are generally considered to be inferior to 'hake' *(Merluccius merluccius* (L.)). There is a similar need to distinguish other species of hake which have been imported into the UK in recent years and which are likely to become of increasing commercial importance. These species are best grouped together as 'Atlantic hake' *(Merluccius hubbsi* (Marini) and *Merluccius bilinearis* (Mitchell)) and 'Pacific hake' *(Merluccius productus* (Ayres) and *Merluccius gayi* (Guich)). We so *recommend*.

223.   *Sardines and pilchards*. We have examined the suggestion made in representations that the name 'sardine' should be allowed in a qualified form such as 'Scottish sardines' to describe small canned sardine-type fish. This is similar to the provisions of the Codex Draft Standard for Canned Sardines and Sardine-Type Products. The Draft Standard restricts the name 'sardine' unqualified to *Sardina pilchardus* (Walbaum) but permits 'X sardines', 'X' being the name of a country, geographical area or the species, and 'sardine style' and 'sardine type', for the following species, or mixtures of species of the same genus having similar organoleptic qualities:

   Sardina pilchardus (Walbaum)
   Sardinops melanosticta, neopilchardus, ocellata, sagax or caerulea
   Sardinella aurita, anchovia, brasiliensis or maderensis
   Clupea harengus
   Clupea antipodum, bassensis or fuegensis
   Sprattus sprattus (Clupea sprattus)
   Hyperlophus vittatus
   Nematalosa vlaminghi

81

Etrumeus microps
Ethmidium maculatus
Engraulis anchoita
Engraulis ringens

We consider however that the name 'sardine' should be reserved exclusively for small fish of the species *Sardina pilchardus* (Walbaum) since this is the name traditionally applied in the UK. Fish of any other species should not be permitted to use the name even if qualified, since this would establish an undesirable precedent. 'Pilchard' should be retained for *Sardina pilchardus* (Walbaum) without the limitation to small fish. We *recommend* accordingly.

224.   The 1970 Labelling of Food Regulations at present distinguish between 'sardine' and 'pilchard' on a size basis, small *Sardina pilchardus* (Walbaum) being designated 'sardine' and any other fish of that species being designated 'pilchard'. This distinction is rather imprecise since 'small' is not defined, but it does not in practice seem to have caused any difficulties. Although we would prefer a greater element of precision to apply, the lack of any practical difficulties has led us to *recommend* that the existing distinction should remain. An indication on the labels of tins of sardines of the range of numbers of fish likely to be present might however be useful for the consumer.

225.   *Sild.* This name is at present required to describe small herring *(Clupea harengus* (L.)). The name 'sild' has for a very long time however applied only to these fish when canned: when fresh or frozen they are described either as 'herring' or, if mixed with sprats, as 'whitebait' (see paragraph 228 below). To avoid the possibility of confusion, however, we *recommend* that 'sild' should in future be restricted to fish which have been canned. This is consistent with our views on 'brisling' in paragraph 227 below.

226.   It has been suggested that 'sild' should apply both to small *Clupea harengus* (L.) and to sprats *(Sprattus sprattus* (L.)) since, when young, shoals of these fish intermix and it is impossible to separate the species on a commercial scale. We consider that this should be recognized as it is for 'whitebait' (paragraph 228 below). We *recommend* that 'sild' should therefore in future be permitted for canned small *Clupea harengus* (L.) and canned small *Sprattus sprattus* (L.).

227.   *Sprat or brisling.* As with the name 'sild', 'brisling' is used exclusively for canned fish. We therefore *recommend* that this practice should continue to be recognised and that 'brisling' should in future be permitted to describe only canned *Sprattus sprattus* (L.).

228.   *Whitebait.* This name is required by the 1970 Labelling of Food Regulations to be applied to young of *Clupea harengus* (L.) and young of *Sprattus sprattus* (L.) and the requirement recognizes traditional usage. Because of difficulties which might occur with the use of the designation 'young', we consider that 'small' should be substituted for it. Although it may be argued that this latter term is as imprecise as 'young', we consider that it

should help to make the requirement less open to differing interpretations. We *recommend* accordingly.

Salmon and freshwater fish

229.   *Bream, carp, char, perch, pike, pikeperch.* We *recommend* that these names may be removed from legislative control since these species are only rarely sold by retail and when they are, there is little likelihood of the wrong name being applied.

230.   *Salmon.* The present requirements of the 1970 Labelling of Food Regulations are that fish of the species *Salmo salar* (L.) be described as 'salmon' and that certain species of the *Oncorhynchus* genus must be described as 'salmon' but always suitably qualified eg 'red salmon', 'pink salmon' according to the species. It has been suggested that all species of *Oncorhynchus* be described simply as 'Canadian salmon' or 'Pacific salmon' when sold fresh or frozen, other qualified names such as 'red salmon' being reserved for the canned fish. Since however these other names are used to indicate quality, ie 'red salmon' is generally regarded as of higher quality than 'pink salmon', their use is equally important whether the fish are canned, fresh or frozen. We therefore *recommend* that no changes are made to this entry.

231.   *Smoked salmon.* Regulation 3(5), proviso (b), permits the use of a traditional name for fish which has been subjected to smoking or any similar process. The name 'smoked salmon' is therefore permitted by virtue of its traditional usage and would appear to be available at present for smoked fish of both the *Salmo* and *Oncorhynchus* species, without the need to distinguish between them as discussed in paragraph 230 above. In practice we understand that there are two common descriptions currently in use — 'smoked salmon' and 'smoked Scotch salmon'. We have been told that the description 'smoked Scotch salmon' may sometimes be used misleadingly to describe the product made from *Oncorhynchus*. Indeed, most smoked salmon is, we were informed, made from fish from the latter genus. The product sold as smoked Scotch salmon is often more expensive than that sold as smoked salmon, mainly because of the greater prestige attached to the name. As a raw material, *Salmo* is usually more expensive than *Oncorhynchus*. We are doubtful whether a consumer would be able to perceive a marked difference in flavour and texture between smoked *Salmo* and smoked *Oncorhynchus* but we consider that the passing-off of *Oncorhynchus* for the more expensive *Salmo* should not be permitted. We therefore *recommend* that the name 'smoked salmon' should be permitted only for *Salmo salar:* smoked fish of the *Oncorhynchus* genus should be described by the appropriate name listed in our revised schedule of fish names at Appendix 4 preceded by the word 'smoked' eg 'smoked coho salmon'.

232.   *Trout.* We have been told that difficulties have been experienced with the use of the names set out in the present Schedule and *recommend* that the following names for trout should be used:

Brown trout — *Salmo trutta* (L.) which has spent all of its life in fresh water

Sea trout (salmon trout) — *Salmo trutta* (L.) which has spent part of its life in sea water

Cut-throat trout — *Salmo clarkii* (Richardson)

Rainbow trout (steelhead trout) — *Salmo gairdneri* (Richardson)

The names in brackets should be phased out eventually in accordance with our views set out in paragraph 218 (c) above.

Shellfish

233. *Shrimps and prawns.* The nomenclature of shrimps and prawns has frequently been a subject for argument and recently a successful prosecution was taken on the basis of 'shrimps' being sold as 'prawns'. The principal difficulty is that opinions vary as to when a 'shrimp' becomes a 'prawn': some consider the difference between the two is one of size alone and this would seem to be the opinion of most consumers, but others consider that differentiation should be on a species basis. The 1970 Labelling of Food Regulations attempt to differentiate both by size and by species as follows:

Name	Species	Alternative Name
Shrimp	—*Pandalus montagui* (Leach) All species of *Crangon* Small fish of:— all species of *Palaemonidae* all species of *Penaeidae* all species of *Pandalidae*	—Pink Shrimp —Brown Shrimp
Prawn	—Large *Pandalus borealis* (Krøyer) Large fish of:— all species of *Palaemonidae* all species of *Penaeidae* all species of *Pandalidae*	—Deepwater Prawn

234. Neither 'large' nor 'small' is defined in the 1970 Regulations and this has led to considerable difficulties since what is 'large' and what is 'small' remains open to widely differing interpretations. This is unsatisfactory, both for the consumer who may not get what he expects, and for the processor, who may be undecided as to the correct name to apply to his products. We therefore decided that for those species which were at present only differentiated by the use of the terms 'large' and 'small', a more positive distinction needed to be drawn. It is generally agreed that *Pandalus montagui* (Leach) and all species of *Crangon* should always be designated 'shrimp' and we make no further reference to these species.

235. There is no scientific distinction between the vernacular terms 'shrimp' and 'prawn' and we were told that in France the single word 'crevette' includes both shrimps and prawns. The Codex Standards for quick frozen and canned

shrimps or prawns also make no distinction between the two. Widely distributed species are sometimes called 'shrimp' in one country and 'prawn' in another. In the United Kingdom traditional and common usage treats 'shrimp' as denoting small specimens and 'prawn' larger specimens. A system of differentiation based on species only would entail, for instance, describing all species of Palaemonidae, Penaeidae and Pandalidae as 'prawns'. Since these species however comprise a wide range of sizes, the name 'prawn' could be used to describe very small specimens which would almost certainly be considered as 'shrimps' by the consumer. Similarly a system allowing all these species to be designated as *either* 'shrimps' or 'prawns' would also lead to similar difficulties since it is likely that, given a choice, manufacturers will prefer always to use the name 'prawn' because of its greater attractiveness to the consumer.

236.   We therefore decided that a distinction should be drawn mainly on size rather than on a species basis. The simplest method of doing this is by count per pound which is the method at present used by the UK trade: differentiation by length seems altogether impractical. But even on this basis opinions varied. Thus, according to our information, some parts of the UK trade distinguished 'prawns' as being all specimens up to a size corresponding to about 800 per pound, cooked and peeled, and 'shrimp' as anything smaller. One enforcement authority suggested a dividing line at 500 per pound peeled. Different forms of presentation such as whole, tails only, fresh, peeled, dried, frozen, pickled and breaded mean inevitably a variation in number per pound, which may be considerable, compared with that for whole fish in the freshly caught condition.

237.   The most sensible and practical method of differentiation seemed to us to be one based on a cut-off point for number per kilogram which would encompass most of those crustaceans which are usually described as 'prawn' in the UK. We were told that inspection of the descriptions at present applied to shrimps and prawns suggests that the smallest species most often called 'prawn' is the common prawn *Palaemon serratus* (Pennant), whose weight ranges from about 0.5g to 16g but whose average weight is around 8-12g, corresponding to a length of about 10cm[48]. Other species of prawns are usually larger. Figures for the yield of peeled, cooked tails (the style most commonly sold to consumers) from the whole animal are not available, but on the reasonable assumption that it is 30%, the corresponding average weight of tail is about 3g ie 330/Kg (150/lb). It is estimated that *Palaemon* of this weight will be about 40mm (1.5 inches) long which is probably about the smallest size the consumer would expect to be called 'prawn'. We therefore *recommend* that the name 'prawn' be used only for Palaemonidae, Penaeidae and Pandalidae with a count of 330/Kg (150/lb) or less peeled, cooked tails: others with a count greater than this should be designated 'shrimp'. It is desirable to set a corresponding count for differentiating between whole shrimps and prawns. The data we have is insufficient for this purpose but we suggest steps should be

---

[48]M R Reeve: Fishery Investigations II, volume 26(i), 1969, p.10.

taken to determine a figure for inclusion in legislation.

Revised Schedule

238. Our revised schedule of fish names, based on the discussion at paragraphs 205-237 above and the principles set out at paragraph 218, is at Appendix 4. A number of minor changes have also been included where this will clarify and rationalize existing requirements and where scientific classification may have changed since the 1970 Labelling of Food Regulations were made. We *recommend* that the revised schedule be used as a basis for future labelling legislation.

VII MISCELLANEOUS MATTERS

Exemptions (Regulation 4)

239.   Regulation 4 of the 1970 Labelling of Food Regulations exempts certain foods from the main requirements of the Regulations. Regulations 4(1)(a) and (b) exempt from all the requirements (except those relating to advertisements) any food intended at the time of sale for export and any food supplied under Government contracts for consumption by Her Majesty's forces or supplied for consumption by visiting armed forces. These exemptions are still necessary, firstly to take account of the need to label differently foods destined for export in order to meet other countries' requirements and, secondly, because food supplied to the armed forces may have to bear different information to meet their particular needs. These exemptions are usually included in all legislation made under the Food and Drugs Acts. We *recommend* their inclusion in any future labelling legislation.

240.   Until 3 January 1983, Regulation 4(2) exempts from the whole of the Regulations 'any bottle containing a drink and bearing a fired-on or embossed, but no other, label' if the bottle were first used for sale before 4 January 1971 and the label complies with appropriate legislation made under the Food and Drugs Act 1955 which was in force on 1 January 1968 or the day the bottle was first used, whichever is the later. This provision is included in the 1970 Labelling of Food Regulations to provide exemption for certain re-usable bottles which are labelled in accordance with the Labelling of Food Order 1953 and which are likely to remain in use for some years. But for Regulation 4(2) they would have to be withdrawn from sale because they did not comply with the requirements of the 1970 Labelling of Food Regulations, even though remaining usable as containers. Provision may need to be made in any new Regulations to continue the exemptions until January 1983 although a shorter period is unlikely to create any serious difficulties. The period of time allowed (some ten years) for this exemption in our view would seem to be excessively long, even recognizing the length of time during which these bottles are likely to remain re-usable. We therefore *recommend* that should any similar exemption be considered necessary in future labelling legislation in relation to containers of this type which are correctly labelled in accordance with the 1970 Regulations, the period of exemption should be a much reduced one. Article 11.3(b) of the EEC Food Labelling Directive (see paragraphs 194 and 203 above) exempts these types of containers from certain provisions for ten years. We consider that this period is also excessive.

241.   Regulations 4(3) to 4(7) have been inserted into the 1970 Labelling of Food Regulations by compositional regulations[49] made to implement EEC directives dealing with specified sugar products, cocoa and chocolate products, honey, fruit juices and fruit nectars and condensed and dried milk. Regulation 4(3) exempts specified sugar products from Part II of the Regulations (general requirements); Regulation 4(4) exempts cocoa products

87

and chocolate products from Parts II and III (general requirements and special requirements applicable to certain foods); Regulation 4(5) exempts honey from Part II; Regulation 4(6) exempts certain fruit juices and fruit nectars from Part II except in relation to listing ingredients; Regulation 4(7) exempts from Part II any condensed or dried milk manufactured after 30 June 1978 other than that intended exclusively for infant feeding. All these foods are therefore exempt from the requirements of Part II of the 1970 Labelling of Food Regulations to give an appropriate designation or common or usual name and the name and address of the labeller or packer and all except fruit juices and fruit nectars will be exempt from ingredient listing. The regulations which control their composition, labelling and advertising (see footnote 49) however require the use of a 'reserved description' which will have similar effect to an appropriate designation; the name and address of the manufacturer or packer must also be declared. The commodity regulations also require declarations of particular ingredients such as the minimum percentage of cocoa solids (for cocoa and chocolate products) but there are no general requirements to declare *all* the ingredients. We discussed this omission in paragraphs 29, 43 and 44 of our Report on Ingredient Listing where we argued against declarations of selected ingredients being used to justify omission of ingredient listing. We saw no reason why a full list could not be given. The requirements for ingredient listing in the EEC Food Labelling Directive will not affect the provisions of these commodity regulations by virtue of Article 20 which exempts from control Community provisions 'relating to the labelling and presentation of certain foodstuffs already adopted' at the time of notification of the Directive. However, we understand that such existing Community requirements will be re-examined as soon as possible to decide whether they should be brought into line with the provisions of the Directive. It is likely that a list of ingredients will eventually be required for all these foods. We urge that steps are taken to consider any exemptions from ingredient listing implicit in EEC commodity directives as speedily as possible.

---

[49]The Specified Sugar Products Regulations
  England and Wales SI 1976 No 509
  Scotland SI 1976 No 946 (S82)
  Northern Ireland SR (NI) 1976 No 165

The Cocoa and Chocolate Products Regulations
  — see footnote 45 Page 73

The Honey Regulations
  England and Wales SI 1976 No 1832
  Scotland SI 1976 No 1818 (S143)
  Northern Ireland SR (NI) 1976 No 387

The Fruit Juices and Fruit Nectars Regulations
  England and Wales SI 1977 No 927
  Scotland SI 1977 No 1026 (S79)
  Northern Ireland SR (NI) 1977 No 182

The Condensed and Dried Milk Regulations
  England and Wales SI 1977 No 928
  Scotland SI 1977 No 1027 (S80)
  Northern Ireland SR (NI) 1977 No 196

The relationship of labels to advertisements

242.   Ideally, the requirements of labelling legislation should as far as is practical be the same for advertisements and labels. It would however be impracticable always to require information such as a list of ingredients in an advertisement but it is essential, if consumers are not to be misled, that controls on descriptions apply equally to labels and advertisements. The parts of the 1970 Labelling of Food Regulations controlling, for instance, the use of the words 'flavour' and 'milk', 'butter' and 'cream' apply equally to advertisements as they do to labels, as already described. Compositional regulations have similar application. In any areas not susceptible to such specific control we consider that the recommendation in paragraph 40 of our 1966 Report on Claims in respect of vitamin and mineral claims (discussed in our Second Report on Claims and Misleading Descriptions) is of relevance. Expanding that recommendation to apply to foods generally, we *recommend* that the phrasing or presentation of any advertisement, whether oral or written, should not in any way be inconsistent with information required to appear on the label of the food to which the advertisement relates.

243.   We shall be returning to this subject, in relation to information required in support of a claim, in our Second Report on Claims and Misleading Descriptions.

Liqueur chocolates

244.   As part of our labelling review we were asked to examine the requirements of Regulation 6(i) of the 1976 Cocoa and Chocolate Products Regulations which relates to the composition of liqueur chocolates. This Regulation generally repeats the provisions of Regulation 13 of the 1970 Labelling of Food Regulations which was revoked by the 1976 Cocoa and Chocolate Products Regulations. Regulation 6(i) requires that any filled chocolate described directly or indirectly on a label or ticket or in an advertisement as a liqueur chocolate must contain 'a liquid filling comprising a significant quantity' of liqueur, spirits or fortified wine. Regulation 7(1)(ii) is also relevant in that it requires any chocolate product other than filled chocolate which bears or includes a declaration of the presence of spirits on the label or ticket or in an advertisement to contain not less than 1% spirits. The form of this requirement, ie 1% spirits, cannot be considered to be very satisfactory.

245.   We received representations that the absence of any quantitative figure for the liquid filling in Regulation 6(i) inhibited enforcement. Reliance solely on a requirement for the filling to be a 'significant quantity' has meant that the 'standard' which ought to be attained has had to depend on an opinion of what was customary and expected by the purchaser. 'Significant quantity' in Regulation 6(i) is not defined and, if interpreted as 'enough to be noticed by the person who eats it', would seem to mean that almost any liqueur chocolates would comply with the Regulation provided there was a quantity of *liquid* filling present, however small. We have been told that, in the absence of

Regulation 6(i), prosecutions could be taken under Section 2 of the Food and Drugs Act 1955 in instances where substantial deficiencies occurred in the filling because the chocolate product would be not of the nature, substance or quality demanded.

246.   The difficulties with the operation of Regulation 6(i) which have been drawn to our attention would seem to point towards the need for establishing by regulation a minimum standard for the quantity of liqueur, spirits or fortified wine which should be present in the filling of any liqueur chocolate. The present requirements stem from the recommendations in paragraph 108 of our 1966 Report on Claims, where we examined the descriptions to be applied to these products. Most liqueur chocolates at that time contained between 0.4 and 1.3 proof gallons per 100 lb of chocolate (1.77% alcohol m/m[50] and 5.73% alcohol m/m[50] respectively) with a mean of 0.9 proof gallons (3.9% alcohol m/m). It has been suggested within the Association of Public Analysts that there should be a minimum of 6% proof spirit (2% alcohol m/m) on the whole product and also a minimum of 15% proof spirit (7.2% alcohol m/m) based on the amount of filling.

247.   With the need for a standard in mind, we asked for information from manufacturers about present manufacturing practice. We were told that there are two types of liqueur chocolates, those in which the spirit is enclosed in a sugar casing inside the chocolate and those in which it is not so enclosed. Evaporation through the sugar casing (where there is one) and the chocolate covering is continuous and the amount of liquid filling will therefore diminish from the time of manufacture onwards. The process will of course be accelerated by any fault in the covering or any damage caused through poor storage or careless handling. We were told that if liqueur chocolates were kept too long at any point in the distributive chain, the liquid filling could eventually disappear. We were also told that the quantity of alcohol derived from any fortified wines, vermouths etc used was likely to be less than that of any spirits or spirituous liqueurs.

248.   We understand that, although not in favour of any statutory standard for liqueur chocolates, manufacturers could conform to a standard of 6% proof spirit on the whole product (2% alcohol m/m) for those containing spirituous liqueurs and 3.5% proof spirit on the whole product (1.2% alcohol m/m) for those containing fortified wines, vermouths, etc. Because of the difficulties with evaporation of the filling, however, it is argued by manufacturers that this standard should apply only at the time of manufacture. In practice, we were informed, most manufacturers incorporate, when making their products, substantially higher amounts than those given above.

249.   We consider that to avoid any future difficulties with this requirement, the 'significant quantity' of liqueur, spirits or fortified wine referred to in

---

[50]The percentage is on a mass/mass basis which in EEC documents is abbreviated to '% mas'.

Regulation 6(i) needs to be defined. We think that a minimum quantity of liquid filling should always be present and not only at the time of manufacture, irrespective of the type of liqueur, spirits or fortified wine used. We therefore *recommend* that any filled chocolate as defined in the 1976 Cocoa and Chocolate Products Regulations, which is described directly or indirectly as 'liqueur chocolates' should contain not less than 2% alcohol m/m on the whole product for those products containing spirits or spirituous liqueurs and 1.2% alcohol m/m on the whole product for those containing fortified wines, vermouths, etc. This standard would mean that similar quantities of liquid would be present in each type of chocolate with those containing, for instance, whisky having a higher alcohol content than those containing sherry, which would be an accurate reflection of the differences between these types of liquors. We appreciate that evaporation will take place but the adoption of date marking will avoid many of the risks inherent in the distribution network.

Instructions for use

250.   Article 3.1(8) of the EEC Food Labelling Directive requires prepacked food to carry instructions for use on the label 'when it would be impossible to make appropriate use of the foodstuff in the absence of such instructions'. We consider that such a requirement is useful in relation to specific foods where the circumstances and individual need can be accurately assessed. The provision in the Directive is too wide and too dependent on subjective judgement to be workable: it is much more relevant to requirements for specific foods or groups of foods. We hope that the provision can therefore be written into UK legislation clearly so as to reduce any problems of interpretation to a minimum. As we said in paragraph 54 above in relation to the requirement in the Directive for a percentage declaration of the main ingredient, we foresee a need for co-operation between manufacturers and enforcement authorities until all concerned become familiar with such a new provision.

VIII SUMMARY OF RECOMMENDATIONS

General labelling principles

251. 1. All future labelling legislation should be based on recommended general labelling principles (paragraph 27).

General labelling provisions

2. *Definitions.* The present exemptions from the definition of 'container' for certain types of packaging for foods such as fresh fruit, vegetables and flour confectionery in the 1970 Labelling of Food Regulations should continue (paragraph 31).

3. Consideration should be given to amending the definition of 'food' in the Food and Drugs Acts to include water (paragraph 32).

4. The labelling provisions of the EEC Food Labelling Directive should be applied to food sold to caterers (paragraph 34).

5. If permitted by the EEC Food Labelling Directive, the definition of 'sell' in the 1970 Labelling of Food Regulations should be retained and the definition 'sell by retail' amended specifically to include selling to a caterer for the purposes of his catering business (paragraph 35).

6. The effect of the present exemption for 'wholly transparent containers' should be retained in any future legislation. The price, the retailer's name and address and the quantity of the food should be permitted to appear on the container without the exemption being lost (paragraph 36).

7. The existing definition of 'label' should be sufficient for the purposes of future labelling legislation (paragraph 37).

8. The definition of 'advertisement' as in Section 135 of the Food and Drugs Act 1955 should be used in future labelling legislation (paragraph 38).

9. Other definitions and provisions in Regulations 2(1) to 2(6) should be retained in legislation (paragraph 39).

10. *Appropriate designation.* The existing definition of 'appropriate designation' should be retained, subject to amendment to include a common or usual name, provided it is made clear that only a common or usual name that is sufficiently well established may be an appropriate designation, always providing that it is not misleading. (This revised definition is referred to subsequently as the *appropriate designation.)* (Paragraphs 41 and 42).

11. The provision for names laid down by other regulations being regarded as appropriate designations should be retained (paragraph 43).

12. The order of ingredients listed in the appropriate designation is controlled successfully by Regulation 3(3) and should be unchanged (paragraph 44).

13. The 'thirty-year rule' should no longer continue (paragraph 45).

14. Statements of purpose eg 'coffee creamer' should always be accompanied by a correct designation (paragraph 47).

15. Negative statements should be accompanied by a description adequate to qualify as an *appropriate designation* (paragraph 48).

16. Prepacked food should continue to be identified by an *appropriate designation* (paragraph 50).

17. *Ingredient listing.* All prepacked food and drinks other than those consisting of a single ingredient and 'any meal' and 'prepacked fresh fruit and vegetables' should be required to bear a full list of ingredients. If suitable generic terms are available which obviate the need for repeated and costly switching of labels, many problems in listing ingredients can be overcome (Appendix 2, paragraph 10).

18. 'Ingredient' should be defined along the lines of the definition in the EEC Food Labelling Directive (Appendix 2, paragraph 10).

19. Alcoholic drinks should not be exempt from any requirement to list ingredients (Appendix 2, paragraph 22).

20. 'Any meal' as at present defined in the 1970 Labelling of Food Regulations should remain totally exempt from the need for a declaration of ingredients when sold to residents of hotels, guest houses, etc. Other sales of such meals should continue to be exempt provided the component foods are listed on a ticket or notice (Appendix 2, paragraph 41).

21. Prepacked fresh fruit and vegetables should remain exempt from ingredient listing providing that with mixed fruit and mixed vegetables the appropriate designation identifies the individual items (Appendix 2, paragraph 42).

22. With boxes of assorted chocolates there may be a need to consider the use of a phrase such as 'These chocolates are made from . . . .'. Selections which contain a number of separate individual products normally sold separately such as chocolate bars should not be required to declare ingredients on the outer wrapper provided the individual items are declared and ingredients are listed on each item of confectionery within the box (Appendix 2, paragraph 30).

23. Where appropriate, generic terms should be available for use by

93

manufacturers to help overcome real labelling difficulties: the coverage of any generic terms allowed should be closely defined and the terms used should be understandable to consumers (Appendix 2, paragraph 47).

24. The number of generic terms used must be kept to the minimum consistent with the need for clear and positive information (paragraph 58).

25. Revised lists of generic terms should appear in any new labelling regulations (Appendix 2, paragraphs 52 and 53).

26. Where an ingredient is made up of two or more constituents, the appropriate designations of those constituents should always appear in immediate proximity to the appropriate designation of the ingredient (paragraph 61).

27. The foods listed in Part III of Schedule 2 to the 1970 Labelling of Food Regulations should form the basis of any new list of exemptions from constituent listing (Appendix 2, paragraph 61).

28. Very small amounts of certain additives which are constituents of ingredients should continue to be declared as 'x with permitted preservative' etc (paragraph 62).

29. Provisions along existing lines for the 'carry-over' of very small amounts of additives should apply to all additives and the effects of the additives should be related to the food rather than the ingredient as in the EEC Food Labelling Directive (paragraph 64).

30. The alternative method of ingredient listing, specifying the quantity or proportion of each ingredient, should continue to be available if permitted by the EEC Food Labelling Directive (paragraph 65).

31. The existing provisions for listing dried ingredients should be maintained. Where an ingredient is placed in the ingredients list as though it had first been reconstituted, the appropriate designation should be qualified by a description such as 'when reconstituted' (paragraph 66).

32. The existing provision for alphabetical listing of ingredients should be maintained. Nuts should be included in this provision (paragraph 67).

33. Ingredients lists should be headed 'Ingredients in weight order'. Other headings referred to in paragraph 68 should be appropriately changed. This supersedes recommendation 23 of our 1977 Report on Beer and recommendation 9 of our Report on Ingredient Listing at Appendix 2 (paragraphs 68 and 69).

34. The requirement for a declaration of additives for certain foods otherwise exempt from ingredient declaration should be retained until such time as full ingredient listing is required for all foods (paragraph 73).

35. If any foods remain exempt from ingredient declaration, consideration should be given to retaining the provision which in certain circumstances requires a full declaration of ingredients if an exempt food carries on the label a reference to any of its ingredients (paragraph 75).

36. *Exemption for the producer/retailer.* Food prepacked by a retailer and sold by him on the premises where it was prepacked or from a delivery van owned by him should be exempt from an ingredient declaration. This exemption should be restricted to food sold from a single premises, which should be defined as 'all buildings at one address'. Flour confectionery in crimp cases should not be regarded as prepacked. The exemption may also cover some supermarkets which do their own prepacking and this should be given further consideration in the light of representations received when drafting future legislation (paragraph 80).

37. Food sold by the producer/retailer as defined in recommendation 36 in wholly transparent containers and marked with the price, quantity and the retailer's name and address should be regarded as non-prepacked (paragraph 81).

38. The producer/retailer should be required to label food he sells with an appropriate designation: this may be by ticket or notice rather than by a label attached to the individual foods (paragraph 82).

39. *The name and address requirement.* The existing requirements for the declaration of the name and address of the packer or labeller or the person on whose behalf the food was packed or labelled should be retained. Proviso (b) to Regulation 5(3) will need to be examined to establish how much intoxicating liquor labelled in accordance with the Labelling of Food Order 1953, and likely to be controlled by future labelling legislation, remains to be sold when that legislation comes into force (paragraph 84).

40. Food prepacked by a retailer and bread and flour confectionery sold by the producer at present exempt from the name and address requirement should continue to be exempt (paragraph 85).

41. Present provisions permitting the omission of the name and address etc from the labels of small containers should not be retained (paragraph 86).

42. *Sales other than by retail.* Foods sold to caterers or cash-and-carry stores should be labelled as for a retail sale. Where food is sold to a manufacturer for the purposes of his business the necessary information, if not appearing on the container, must be made available to the purchaser within fourteen days (paragraphs 87 and 88).

43. *Non-prepacked foods.* All non-prepacked food when sold by retail

95

should be identified by its *appropriate designation* by means of a ticket or other suitable method of identification such as on a menu, a price list or other document clearly displayed in the shop or in a catering establishment (paragraph 94).

44. The provisions requiring a declaration of additives for certain non-prepacked foods should continue. The additives listed in Regulation 9(2), together with mineral hydrocarbons, should continue to be declared. Additives present in a non-prepacked food only because of their use in an ingredient need not be declared, but only where the amount present does not have any significant effect on the food (paragraphs 96 and 97).

45. *Advertisement of food for sale from vending machines.* The present provisions should be retained (paragraph 99).

46. *Use of the word 'flavour'.* If the name of a food is used in an appropriate designation to indicate a specific flavour, that flavour must be derived *wholly* from the food indicated by that name. If any of the flavour is derived from artificial flavour, the word 'flavour' must immediately follow the name of the food in letters of the same size, style and colour. No pictures of the natural food should be allowed where the flavour is not derived wholly from that food. The shape of a container should not suggest a particular fruit etc if the flavour of that fruit is at all imparted by artificial flavour (paragraph 102).

47. Where a food is described as 'X flavour' in accordance with recommendation 46, the words :'contains artificial flavour' should appear in close proximity to the appropriate designation in letters of the same size, style and colour (paragraph 103).

48. *Use of the word 'chocolate'.* The word 'chocolate' should be allowed to be used in the name of any food if that food contains not less than 2.5% non-fat cocoa solids. If less, the words 'flavoured with cocoa solids' or a similar statement must be used (paragraph 106).

Specific requirements for particular foods

49. *Prepacked and non-prepacked butchers' meat and offal (excluding poultry).* The *appropriate designation* required for both prepacked and non-prepacked butchers' meat (excluding poultry) should include an indication of the true name of the cut or joint as appropriate. 'Cut' should be extended to include indications of use: where any doubt or ambiguity arises there are advantages in labelling with a 'name of cut' in anatomical terms as well as an indication of use. The requirement to give an *appropriate designation* should only apply to such meat and offal exposed for sale in a display area (paragraph 109).

50. The name of the cut or joint to be applied to butchers' meat should be listed in a code of practice rather than regulations (paragraph 110).

51. Butchers' meat and offal which has been frozen and then thawed for retail sale should be labelled or ticketed as appropriate to indicate this (paragraph 113).

52. *Fresh fruit and vegetables.* To avoid difficulties with overlapping legislation, fresh fruit and vegetables covered by EEC grading regulations should be exempt from future labelling legislation (paragraph 119).

53. Of the produce not covered by EEC grading regulations, a declaration of variety should be required for potatoes and melons (paragraph 120).

54. *Concentrated acetic acid.* Existing labelling provisions should be retained although consideration should be given to their inclusion in other legislation (paragraph 125).

55. *Dried or dehydrated foods.* The provisions relating to the description of dried or dehydrated foods should be retained (paragraph 127).

56. *Dry mixes.* Existing requirements should be retained: the only change should be that the letters in the statement 'Add Y' should be at least three-quarters the height of the largest letter (other than an initial letter) in the appropriate designation (paragraph 132).

57. The appropriate designation for dried soup should be 'soup mix', suitably qualified to indicate the type of soup (paragraph 133).

58. Dry mixes, where none of the major ingredients of the final product are present and which are to be added for instance to meat and/or vegetables to produce stews, casseroles etc should be described as 'seasoning mix' or some other similarly unambiguous description (paragraph 134).

59. Despite the introduction of complete custard powders requiring the addition only of water, the exemption for custard powder from the requirement to state 'add milk' on the label should remain (paragraph 135).

60. *Intoxicating and other liquor.* The effects of existing and forthcoming EEC wine regulations on the control and use of the names applied to intoxicating liquor are likely to be significant and any changes in appropriate designation requirements now may be premature. The existing provisions should therefore be retained in respect of alcoholic liquor not controlled by EEC regulations (paragraph 140).

61. Subject to the requirements of EEC wine regulations, provisions requiring labels of intoxicating liquor to bear the name and address of the packer or labeller etc should be retained (paragraph 141).

62. All beverages with an alcohol content in excess of 18% should declare the alcohol content. The general principle of declaration for all intoxicating liquor should be recognized and eventually implemented (paragraph 146).

63. The declaration 'not made from fruit' for undistilled fermented liquor not derived wholly or partly from fruit need not be retained (paragraph 147).

64. The provisions for the labelling of certain spirits of less than 65 per cent proof spirit should be deleted (paragraph 148).

65. When changes are made to the 1970 Labelling of Food Regulations to reflect EEC limitation on the use of the word 'wine', it will be important to ensure that provision is made for the continued use of traditional products such as orange wine, ginger wine and elderberry wine and for the sale of home-made wine kits. The use of 'non-alcoholic wine' to describe sacramental or communion wine should also be protected (paragraphs 152 and 159).

66. 'Vin de liqueur' should be required to contain a minimum of 15% alcohol by volume to reflect recent changes in the Common Customs Tariff. The reference in Regulation 17(iii) to 'sucrose, dextrose or invert sugar' should be replaced by 'any sugar' with sugar being defined as 'any carbohydrate sweetening matter' (paragraph 153).

67. The use of the word 'champagne' should no longer be controlled by labelling regulations (paragraph 154).

68. The use of the word 'vintage' in relation to cider should no longer be allowed (paragraph 155).

69. No changes should be made to the existing requirements for the alcohol content of shandies although the provisions in the Regulations should be simplified (paragraph 157).

70. Legislation should not stand in the way of the sale of 'dealcoholised' wine provided it is suitably labelled. Where a particular type of wine has been used as a basis for the product, an appropriate designation of that type of wine should be included as part of the description, which might take the form 'dealcoholised wine made from 'x'', where 'x' is the appropriate designation of the complete wine from which the alcohol has been removed. A declaration of alcoholic strength should also be required (paragraph 160).

71. *Foods contact frozen with liquid freezant.* Requirements for the labelling of food which has been frozen with dichlorodifluoromethane should be retained. The declaration of freezant should take the form 'contact frozen with liquid freezant dichlorodifluoromethane'. The word 'permitted' may precede 'liquid freezant'. In the list of ingredients the generic term 'liquid freezant' may be used (paragraphs 165 and 166).

72. *Processed peas.* The provisions for the labelling and advertising of canned or frozen peas which have been dried or soaked prior to canning or freezing should be retained. The description 'processed peas' should be retained in future legislation. The descriptions 'fresh', 'garden', or 'green' should no longer be permitted to describe any peas which have been dried (paragraph 169).

73. *Canned garden peas with sulphur dioxide added in place of colouring matter.* There should be no further separate labelling requirements for canned garden peas with sulphur dioxide added in place of colouring matter either in the form of a different appropriate designation or a special declaration of additives. Any declaration drawing attention to the absence of colouring matter in these products should be accompanied by an indication of all the additives present in immediate proximity to the appropriate designation (paragraph 172).

74. *Use of the words 'milk', 'butter' and 'cream'.* Provisions relating to the use of the word 'milk' should be retained as should provisions relating to the use of the word 'butter' in *sugar confectionery, chocolate confectionery* and *filled chocolates* (paragraphs 174 and 175).

75. Existing controls should be extended to cover the use of the word 'butter' in *flour confectionery* and *biscuits*. A reference to 'butter' in the name of a cake should be allowed only if all the added fat is butterfat: a reference to 'butter' in the name of a biscuit should be allowed only if at least two-thirds of the fat is butterfat. Cakes containing only a proportion of butter should be permitted to carry sub-designations such as 'containing butter' only if butter constitutes a minimum of 5% of the cake crumb (paragraph 177).

76. Existing controls in relation to the use of the word 'cream' in *sugar confectionery* and *chocolate confectionery* should be retained (paragraph 182).

77. Consideration should be given to the deletion of provisions controlling imitation cream and artificial cream in Section 47 of the Food and Drugs Act 1955 (and the equivalent provisions of the Scottish and Northern Ireland Acts) and the inclusion of provisions to control imitation cream in regulations. Provisions controlling reconstituted cream should be dropped (paragraph 184).

78. Existing controls on the use of the words 'milk', 'butter' and 'cream' may be more appropriate for specific compositional regulations (paragraph 185).

Manner of Marking

79. Existing general requirements should be retained (paragraph 197).

80. If permitted by the EEC Food Labelling Directive, future labelling legislation should require that the list of ingredients appear on labels within a surrounding line (paragraph 199).

81. If permitted by the EEC Food Labelling Directive, existing detailed manner of marking requirements should be retained in a code of practice (paragraph 201).

82. The provisions of the EEC Food Labelling Directive relating to bottles with indelible markings should be examined to establish the extent to which existing provisions for soft drinks bottles may be retained (paragraph 203).

83. The provision requiring information to be given on the outermost container or visible through that container should be retained (paragraph 204).

Fish names

84. The existing system of control should continue (paragraph 212).

85. There is no need for a definition of fish product in future labelling legislation (paragraph 216).

86. The use of general descriptions such as 'flat fish fillets' should not be provided for as a substitute for species indications (paragraph 216).

87. 'Black halibut' should be the name applied to *Reinhardtius hippoglossoides* (Walbaum) (paragraph 220).

88. Fish of the species *Anarhichas* should be described as 'catfish' (paragraph 221).

89. 'Hake' should be reserved for *Merluccius merluccius* (L.): 'Cape hake' should be the name required for *Merluccius capensis* (Castelnau) and *Merluccius paradoxus* (Franca): 'Atlantic hake' should be the name for *Merluccius hubbsi* (Marini) and *Merluccius bilinearis* (Mitchell): 'Pacific hake' should be the name for *Merluccius productus* (Ayres) and *Merluccius gayi* (Guich) (Paragraph 222).

90. 'Sardine' and 'pilchard' should be reserved exclusively for fish of the species *Sardina pilchardus* (Walbaum). The present limitation on a size basis for 'sardines' should be retained (paragraphs 223 and 224).

91. 'Sild' should in future be used for small *Clupea harengus*. (L.) and small *Sprattus sprattus* (L.) but only when canned (paragraphs 225 and 226).

92. 'Brisling' should be permitted to describe only canned *Sprattus sprattus* (L.).

93. 'Whitebait' should be applied to small *Clupea harengus* (L.) and small *Sprattus sprattus* (L.) other than canned (paragraph 228).

94. 'Bream', 'carp', 'char', 'perch', 'pike' and 'pikeperch' may be removed from control by Labelling Regulations (paragraph 229).

95. No changes should be made to existing controls on the name 'salmon'. 'Smoked salmon' should however be permitted only for *Salmo salar* (L.): smoked fish of the *Oncorhynchus* genus should be described by the appropriate qualified name eg 'smoked coho salmon' (paragraphs 230 and 231).

96. The names applied to trout should be:

Brown trout — *Salmo trutta* (L.) which has spent all of its life in fresh water

Sea trout (salmon trout) — *Salmo trutta* (L.) which has spent part of its life in sea water

Cut-throat trout — *Salmo clarkii* (Richardson)

Rainbow trout (Steelhead trout) — *Salmo gairdneri* (Richardson) (paragraph 232).

97. The names applied to shrimps and prawns should be:

Shrimp or pink shrimp — *Pandalus montagui* (Leach)

Shrimp or brown shrimp — All species of *Crangon*

Shrimp — fish with a count greater than 330/kg (150/lb) peeled, cooked tails of —

All species of *Palaemonidae*

All species of *Penaeidae*

All species of *Pandalidae*

Prawn — fish with a count of 330/kg (150/lb) or less peeled, cooked tails of —

All species of *Palaemonidae*

All species of *Penaeidae*

All species of *Pandalidae* (paragraph 237).

98. The revised schedule of fish names at Appendix 4 should be used as a basis for future labelling legislation (paragraph 238).

Miscellaneous matters

99. *Exemptions.* Existing exemptions for food intended for export and food supplied to the armed forces should be retained (paragraph 239). The period of any future exemption for bottles with fired-on or embossed labels should be much reduced (paragraph 240).

100. *The relationship of labels to advertisements.* The phrasing or presentation of any oral or written advertisement should not in any way be inconsistent with information required to appear on the label of the food to which the advertisement relates (paragraph 242).

101. *Liqueur chocolates.* Any filled chocolate as defined in the 1976 Cocoa and Chocolate Products Regulations described as 'liqueur chocolates' should contain not less than 2% alcohol m/m on the whole product for those containing spirits or spirituous liqueurs and 1.2% alcohol m/m on the whole product for those containing fortified wines, vermouths etc (paragraph 249).

FSC/REP/69   July 1979

APPENDIX 1

LIST OF ORGANISATIONS AND INDIVIDUALS FROM WHOM EVIDENCE HAS BEEN RECEIVED

Enforcement Authorities and Related Interests

Association of County Councils
Association of County Councils in Scotland
Association of District Councils
Association of Local Authorities of Northern Ireland
Association of Metropolitan Authorities
Association of Public Analysts
Association of Sea and Air Port Health Authorities
A C Bushnell, M Chem A, FRIC
Bolsover District Council
Buckinghamshire County Council
Convention of Scottish Local Authorities
Cornwall County Council
J C Dakin, BSc, MIBiol, FIFST
Hampshire County Council
Hereford and Worcester County Council
Hertfordshire County Council
Institute of Trading Standards Administration
Kent County Council
Royal Borough of Kingston Upon Thames
Lancashire County Council
Local Authorities' Joint Advisory Committee on Standards
London Borough of Enfield
London Borough of Hackney
London Borough of Haringey
London Borough of Newham
G S Meadows, M Chem A, MPhA, FRIC
Mid Glamorgan County Council
Muter and Hackman
Norfolk County Council
North East Regional Analytical Service
Northamptonshire County Council
City of Portsmouth
Salop County Council
South Yorkshire Metropolitan County Council
Staffordshire County Council
Surrey County Council
Warwickshire County Council
West Glamorgan County Council
West Yorkshire Metropolitan County Council
Western Group Public Health Committee

Consumer and Representative Organisations

British Diabetic Association
British Diabetic Association — Wirral Parents' Group
Coeliac Society
Consumers' Association
Consumers' Association of South Humberside
Court of the Chief Rabbi
European Community of Consumer Co-operatives
Farm and Food Society
Food and Agriculture Organisation of the United Nations
Friends of the Earth
International Organisation of Consumers' Unions
E E March
McCarrison Society
Miss V I Mitchell
National Federation of Consumer Groups
National Society for Phenylketonuria
J G Parker
D L Phillips
H H Ransley
Royal Hospital of Saint Bartholomew
H S Smith
A Ward Gardner

Organisations and Individuals Associated with Food Production or Distribution

Advanced Sweeteners Ltd.
Arnold Services
Association of Butter Blenders and Butter and Cheese Packers
Association of Cheese Processors
Australian Canned Fruit (IMO) UK Ltd.
Bacon and Meat Manufacturers' Association
Bakery Allied Traders' Association
W A Baxter & Sons Ltd.
Beecham Foods
Belfast Flour Millers' Association
J Bibby & Sons Ltd.
Boots Co. Ltd.
Brewers' Society
British Association of Canned Food Importers and Distributors
British Essence Manufacturers' Association
British Fish Canners (Fraserburgh) Ltd.
British Food Manufacturing Industries' Research Association
British Frozen Food Federation
British Hotels, Restaurants and Caterers' Association
British Soft Drinks Council
British Sugar Corporation

2

Butter Information Council
Cake and Biscuit Alliance Ltd.
Cocoa, Chocolate and Confectionery Alliance
Coffee Trade Federation
Parliamentary Committee of the Co-operative Union Ltd.
Colman Foods
Courtaulds Ltd.
CPC (United Kingdom) Ltd.
Farley Health Products Ltd.
Federation of Bakers
Fisons Ltd.
Flour Milling and Baking Research Association
Food Manufacturers' Federation Incorporated
Fresh Fruit and Vegetable Information Bureau
Gin Rectifiers' and Distillers' Association
Ice Cream Alliance
Ice Cream Federation
Imperial Chemical Industries Ltd.
Incorporated National Association of British and Irish Millers
Institute of Practitioners in Advertising
London and National Provision Exchange Ltd.
Lyons Maid Ltd.
Lyons Tetley Ltd.
Margarine and Shortening Manufacturers' Association
Marks and Spencer Ltd.
Meat and Livestock Commission
Michael Peters & Partners Ltd.
Milk Marketing Board
Milk Marketing Board for Northern Ireland
Multiple Food and Drink Retailers' Association
National Association of British Wine Producers
National Association of Cider Makers
National Association of Creamery Proprietors and Wholesale Dairymen
    (Incorporated)
National Association of Master Bakers, Confectioners and Caterers
National Association of Perry Makers
National Federation of Fishmongers Ltd.
National Federation of Fruit & Potato Trades
National Union of Licensed Victuallers
Ormeau Bakery Ltd.
Port Wine Trade Association
Pre-Packed Flour Association
Produce Packaging and Marketing Association
RHM Foods Ltd.
Roche Products Ltd.
Schweppes Ltd.
Scotch Whisky Association
Scottish Association of Master Bakers

Scottish Milk Marketing Board
Scottish Union of Bakers and Allied Workers
Sherry Shippers' Association
Slimming Aid Co. Ltd.
Smedley-HP Foods Ltd.
Smith Kendon Ltd.
Tate and Lyle Ltd.
Tesco Group of Companies
UK Association of Frozen Food Producers
Van den Berghs & Jurgens Ltd.
Vereniging Ter Bevordering Van De Export Van Vleeswaren
Vodka Trade Association
Wander Pharmaceuticals
Welfare Foods (Stockport) Ltd.
Wine and Spirit Association of Great Britain
HF & IC Woolrich Ltd.

Other Interests

Advertising Standards Authority*
British Dietetic Association
British Nutrition Foundation
Douglas R S Haig
Stephen Halliday
Institute of Food Science and Technology
Professor I Macdonald, MD, DSc*
National Economic Development Office — Hotels and Catering EDC
Torry Research Station
Professor A S Truswell, MB, ChB, MD, FRCP, MFCM*
Alan Turner, M Phil, M Chem A, FRIC, FIFST

---

*Gave oral evidence

MINISTRY OF AGRICULTURE, FISHERIES AND FOOD

FOOD STANDARDS COMMITTEE REVIEW OF FOOD LABELLING PART II

EXEMPTIONS FROM INGREDIENT LISTING AND GENERIC TERMS

FSC/REP/69B

September 1977

FOOD STANDARDS COMMITTEE

The terms of reference of the Food Standards Committee are:

To advise the Minister of Agriculture, Fisheries and Food, the Secretary of State for Social Services, the Secretary of State for Scotland and the Head of the Department of Health and Social Services for Northern Ireland, on the composition, description, labelling and advertising of food with particular reference to the exercise of powers conferred on Ministers by Sections 4, 5 and 7 of the Food and Drugs Act 1955 and the corresponding provisions in enactments relating to Scotland and Northern Ireland.

The following served on the Food Standards Committee during the preparation of this report:—

Professor A G WARD, CBE, MA, F Inst P, FIFST (Chairman)
Professor R J L ALLEN, OBE, MSc, PhD
M A CHAPMAN, MBE, FITSA, MBIM
J G COLLINGWOOD, DSc (Hon), BSc, C Eng, FI Chem E
R A DALLEY, M Chem A, C Chem, FRIC, FIFST
H EGAN, BSc, PhD, DIC, C Chem, FRIC, FRSH, FIFST
J A O'KEEFE, OBE, BSc (Econ), LLB, Barrister at Law, FITSA
R PASSMORE, MA, MD, FRCP (Edin)
Mrs G L S PIKE, CBE, JP
Miss R STEPHEN, MBE
F WOOD, MBE, BSc, C Eng, FI Chem E, FIFST

Joint Secretaries

Mrs A M WATERS
J R PARK, BSc, PhD (until October 1976)
I M V ADAMS, ANCFT, FIFST (from November 1976)

CONTENTS

INTRODUCTION

1.   In January 1975 we were asked to review the labelling and advertising of food. This is the first full review since our Report on Food Labelling[1] published in 1964. Following the announcement of the review we received detailed representations from the organisations and individuals listed in the Appendix to this Report. A comprehensive Report on Food Labelling, to be issued at a later date, will discuss the general approach the Committee has adopted, how this approach relates to the Labelling of Food Regulations 1970, as amended[2], the probable effects of the EEC directive on food labelling (or the latest draft available) and the directions future policy should follow. It will also cover many more detailed points, some concerned with the labelling of specific commodities.

2.   Although consideration of the whole area of our review is not yet complete, recent developments in discussions on the EEC draft directive on food labelling suggest that publication of our views on particular aspects of labelling, in advance of a full Report on Food Labelling, would assist discussions and also ensure that our views would be available for wider comment before the draft directive had been finally accepted. Having already issued a Report on the Change from Calorie to Joule in Food Energy Declarations[3] and Part I of our labelling review dealing with the Use of Fructose in Foods Specially Prepared for Diabetics[4], the next major aspect of food labelling to be completed was our examination of exemptions from ingredient listing and the related question of generic terms. Our views and recommendations on these two areas are the subject of the present Report. Further Reports on other aspects of labelling will follow.

Labelling of Food Regulations 1970 (as amended)[2]

3.   It is a general requirement of these Regulations that prepacked foods must bear a full list of ingredients in descending order by weight at the stage at which they were used in the manufacturing process. Certain specified foods however are not required to bear a list of ingredients by virtue of Regulations 4 (3), (4) and (5), and Regulations 5 (1), 6 (1) and 16 although some of these are required to bear a declaration of certain additives (Regulation 7). Exemption from ingredient declaration is given for a variety of reasons, the principal reason originally being the existence of regulations which controlled the composition of the food. Foods exempt for this reason are at present:

---

[1] Food Standards Committee Report on Food Labelling: HMSO 1964

[2] England and Wales SI 1970 No 400 as amended by SI 1972 No 1510 and SI 1976 No 859
    Scotland SI 1970 No 1127 (S 91) as amended by SI 1972 No 1790 (S 141) and 1976 No 1176 (S 102)
    Northern Ireland SR and O (NI) 1970 No 80 as amended by SR and O (NI) 1972 No 318 and SR (NI) 1976 No 212

[3] Food Standards Committee Report on the Change from Calorie to Joule in Food Energy Declarations: FSC/REP/67: MAFF 1976

[4] Food Standards Committee Review of Food Labelling: Part I: The Use of Fructose in Foods Specially Prepared for Diabetics: FSC/REP/69A: MAFF 1977

Artificial sweetening tablets
Bread (not including bread-crumbs)
Butter
Cheese (not including processed cheese and cheese spread)
Cocoa and chocolate products
Condensed milk
Coffee and chicory mixtures including French coffee
Coffee with fig flavour or fig seasoning, including Viennese coffee
Curry powder
Dried milk
Edible gelatine
Flour (including self-raising flour)
Honey
Ice-cream (including dairy ice-cream and milk ice)
Parev or Kosher ice
Specified sugar products

Of these, honey and most specified sugar products are essentially single ingredient foods. Other foods are exempt because at that time it was considered that there were major difficulties for manufacturers and little advantage to consumers in a declaration of ingredients. These are:

Intoxicating liquor
Biscuits
Chocolate confectionery
Flour confectionery
Sugar confectionery

Of the remaining exemptions, fresh fruit and vegetables are either essentially single ingredient foods or are usually sold in such a way that the different types of fruits or vegetables can be clearly seen. The category covered by the term 'any meal' presents particular problems in listing ingredients. Such meals are usually packed lunches provided by hotels or guest houses and are discussed in paragraph 41 below.

4.   A further requirement of the 1970 Labelling of Food Regulations is that, when an ingredient list is required, an 'appropriate designation' of each ingredient must be given. 'Appropriate designation' is defined in Regulation 3(1) as 'a specific (and not generic) name or description which will indicate to an intending purchaser the true nature of the ingredient . . . to which it is applied'. Certain ingredients may however be described by a generic term rather than an appropriate designation. These generic terms and the foods for which they may be used are given in paragraphs 1-3 of Schedule 2 to the Regulations. It is not necessary, for instance, to list muscatels, raisins, sultanas and currants separately: these may be described as 'vine fruits' when an ingredient of a food other than a beverage. We have in our Reports on The Pre-1955 Compositional Orders[5],Offals in Meat Products[6],Yoghurt[7] and Beer[8] recommended some additional generic terms to those listed in the Regulations: these terms are discussed later in the present Report. Certain foods listed in Part III of Schedule 2 to the 1970 Labelling of Food Regulations when used as

an ingredient of another food are exempt from a declaration of their constituents. We deal with these in paragraphs 59-61.

EEC Draft Directive on Food Labelling

5.   Article 6 of the most recent draft of this directive which we have seen requires ingredients to be listed, the following foods as described in the directive being exempted:

single ingredient foods

fresh fruit and vegetables which have not been peeled, cut or similarly treated

beverages produced through alcoholic fermentation — including liqueur wines — and potable spirits

rectified alcohol, the alcoholic strength of which may have been reduced to make it fit for direct consumption

fermented vinegars derived exclusively from a single basic product

cheese
butter
fermented milk
$\left\{\begin{array}{l}\text{'provided no ingredient has been added other than lactic}\\\text{products, enzymes and micro-organism cultures}\\\text{essential to manufacture or other than the salt needed}\\\text{for the manufacture of cheese other than fresh cheese}\\\text{and processed cheese' (for these the ingredient list is}\\\text{intended to consist of the final food (eg yogurt) and the}\\\text{names of any foods or substances added to it (eg}\\\text{strawberries, colours, flavours, preservatives)).}\end{array}\right.$

6.   Generic terms are listed in Annexes I and II to the draft directive: each of these terms is discussed in the body of this Report.

Exemptions from Ingredient Listing

7.   *General.* Before considering the justification for exempting particular foods or classes of foods from ingredient listing, we first examined in detail the principle of exemption. We bore in mind the views expressed in paragraphs 60-70 of our 1964 Report on Food Labelling, the requirements of the 1970 Labelling of Food Regulations and the provisions in the EEC draft directive on food labelling.

8.   Since our 1964 review of food labelling there has been a change in attitude towards the information which appears on food labels. Retail facilities have changed so that an increasing amount of food is sold through self-service outlets where it is likely that the only information available to the purchaser about the food will be that appearing on the label. No longer can the shopper seek information and assistance from the person behind the counter. With this development in the retail trade has also come an increasing consumer interest in food labels and about the ingredients of food offered for sale. The current availability of prepacked food has induced many consumers to read food labels much more diligently than before and to seek more information about particular aspects of those foods in which they are interested. We therefore see every reason why information which can be useful to a substantial number of

7

consumers should be made available on food labels. We discuss later the need to avoid requiring ingredient listing in such a way that major difficulties and substantial fresh costs would arise for manufacturers.

9.   We have in the past accepted, although with increasing reluctance, the argument that when the composition of a food is controlled by law, then the consumer is adequately protected in relation to that composition and there is no need to require information about the ingredients to appear on the label. We have however for some time believed that it is no longer a defensible argument to propose to a consumer, who may be a busy housewife, that to discover the ingredients of for example bread or ice-cream she should visit the public library or buy the appropriate food standards regulation from HM Stationery Office. Still less is the consumer in a position to know and appreciate why some foods have been exempted from the requirement. The consumer wants, justifiably, to be made aware of the ingredients of those foods controlled by regulations in just the same way as she is made aware of the ingredients of other foods on sale on adjacent shelves in the store.

10.   We accept the general argument put forward by food manufacturers that ingredient listing poses problems for some foods. These problems have become particularly acute with wide changes in the cost and availability of raw materials. The fluctuations which occur require a flexible policy of substitution to avoid unduly high price rises or an unsatisfactory product. The problems are, of course, common to those manufacturers whose products already have to bear a list of ingredients as well as to those whose products are exempt. We believe that if suitable generic terms are available, which obviate the need for repeated and costly switching of labels, many problems can be overcome. The experience of other countries has shown that listing ingredients is a practical proposition for all prepacked foods. Additionally certain manufacturers have chosen to list the ingredients of some exempt foods in the United Kingdom. We therefore *recommend* that all prepacked foods and drinks, other than those consisting of a single ingredient, should be required to bear a full list of ingredients. Two special cases for which we consider different provisions are required are discussed in paragraphs 41 and 42. We also *recommend* that 'ingredient' be defined along the lines of the current definition in the EEC draft directive on food labelling as follows:—

>"Ingredient" means any substance, including additives, used in the manufacture or preparation of a food and still present in part or wholly in the finished product, even if in altered form.

Under this definition, water would be regarded as an ingredient and would have to be declared. Although a natural ingredient of all foods, it does not have to be declared under existing legislation. We have dealt with both the special status of water as an ingredient and the declaration of added water in an ingredient list in our separate review of water in food. Our Report on that subject will be published shortly.

11.   We were asked by interested parties to consider the exemption from ingredient listing of those foods whose appropriate designation referred to all

the ingredients present, eg peanuts and raisins. We consider, however, that in such cases it is important that a list of ingredients is provided to inform the consumer that no other ingredient is present. Products sold under the same appropriate designation such as tuna in olive oil may for instance have additional ingredients such as salt and the consumer should always have a ready means of comparison by way of the ingredients list.

12.   We are aware that the absence in law of a definition of a single ingredient food has presented some difficulties in the enforcement of the 1970 Labelling of Food Regulations. The inclusion of a definition of 'ingredient' as suggested in paragraph 10 in any future legislation should however help to clarify the present situation. Bacon and ham, for example, could no longer be generally regarded as single ingredient foods and any curing salts and other additions including water would have to be declared in the ingredients list.

13.   It has been drawn to our attention that the listing of ingredients which are subject to seasonal fluctuations could present difficulties at certain times of the year. We do not consider that these difficulties justify exemption from declarations: the use of permitted generic terms or suitable phrases should enable any such problems to be overcome. We make further reference to this in paragraphs 55-57.

14.   Our recommendation in paragraph 10, if accepted, would ensure that a consistent approach to ingredient listing is followed. This would clarify a situation which, to consumers, must often be confusing whereby similar products may have labels which carry very different amounts of information.

15.   We recognise that some exemptions from ingredient declaration are provided in the EEC draft directive on food labelling and that it is probable that some of these exemptions will be contained in the eventual directive which Member States will adopt. It is not our view that these exemptions are justified or necessary. We emphasise that, as a matter of principle, there should no longer be any exemptions from ingredient declaration. We cannot recommend the adoption of the exemptions in the current draft.

16.   *Specific foods.* Applying the principle expressed in paragraph 10 we have examined in detail each of the foods at present exempt from ingredient declaration under the 1970 Labelling of Food Regulations. Interested parties were asked to comment in relation to these foods after being informed of our general view on exemptions. We have also examined those foods specifically exempt under the provisions of the EEC draft directive on food labelling but which are not currently exempt under the 1970 Labelling of Food Regulations. Foods falling in either of these two groups are discussed in detail below.

17.   *Alcoholic drinks.* Under the 1970 Labelling of Food Regulations there is no requirement for such drinks to bear a list of ingredients. The latest draft of the EEC directive on food labelling we have seen appears to exempt all alcoholic drinks (see paragraph 5). We received many very detailed submissions

9

concerning alcoholic drinks from the relevant sectors of the industry and further comments from enforcement bodies and consumer organisations. The arguments in favour of an ingredients list appearing on all food labels which we discussed in paragraphs 8-10 are, we believe, just as valid for alcoholic drinks as for all other foods. Consumer organisations and enforcement bodies clearly tended to think similarly and sought the same provision of information on alcoholic drinks as on other foods. The view of the industry was very different and all parts argued strongly against the provision of such information. The first arguments put forward were those of practical difficulty. It was said that all alcoholic drinks were made from raw, natural products and as these varied from year to year and even within the same season the ingredients would have to vary to keep the character of the end product constant. Consumers would be confused into thinking that the change in the list of ingredients denoted a change in the drink, when this would not be the case. False comparisons could be made between, for example, perry with added malic acid and that without, when the real picture was that a deficiency in natural malic acid in one product was being corrected. This argument can be made for many foods where there is a seasonal change in ingredients which would occasion an additional item in the ingredients list. We make further reference to this in paragraphs 55-57. It does not appear to us to be a valid argument against ingredient listing for alcoholic drinks.

18.   It was submitted that some alcoholic drinks such as whisky and sherry were, as sold, a blend of several long matured ingredients of unknown quantitative composition. A requirement to list the ingredients and therefore to know the relative amounts of each ingredient was impossible. It seems to us that this is a practical problem only when the basic substance from which the alcohol is made varies between the ingredients of the blend, for example, if a blend of whiskies is made from individual whiskies resulting from the fermentation of different cereals. Even in such cases we find it difficult to believe that the relationships necessary to produce an ingredients list cannot readily be calculated without serious error. Only the order of listing is in question, so that precise figures of ingredient amounts are unnecessary.

19.   It has also been argued that for a variety of reasons the amounts of certain minor ingredients may change temporarily so that the order of these on the label might not always be accurate. We recognise the difficulty but doubt whether in these circumstances a lack of accuracy will be of any detriment to consumers since the order of the major ingredients will not be affected. Similar circumstances are likely to occur occasionally with other foods and we are sure that enforcement authorities in such a situation can be relied on to continue to exercise their customary discretion.

20.   Other arguments of practical difficulty were also put forward but these tended to be the same as for other sectors of the food industry facing the question of ingredient listing for the first time. They included the need to redesign long used labels, the possibility of giving away secret and traditional recipes and the cost, which would eventually have to be passed on to the

consumer. The number of generic terms already available to manufacturers goes some way to masking the finer detail of a recipe, as does also the lack of quantitative declaration.

21.   However, other arguments were put forward which were peculiar to alcoholic drinks. One of the most important of these was that alcoholic drinks were the products of very extensive fermentation and that to list the original ingredients would be to mislead the consumer, who might expect to find hops and barley in a bottle of beer and would not understand that the chemical changes during fermentation would have substantially transformed the original ingredients. We considered this problem in our Report on Beer where, to help the consumer to understand the situation, we recommended that the ingredients list be headed 'Brewed from', rather than 'Ingredients' as required by the 1970 Labelling of Food Regulations. A similar change could accommodate other alcoholic beverages. We therefore *recommend* that the term 'Ingredients used' head ingredients lists for these, carrying with it the idea that the materials which were originally present do not necessarily remain in the final product. When applied to alcoholic drinks, the term 'Ingredients used' would obviate the need for other terms such as 'Distilled from', 'Blended from' etc which might have been necessary to take proper account of different methods of production when listing ingredients. While the term 'Ingredients' is legally clear it is hoped that the addition of the word 'used' will convey to the consumer the conditions under which ingredients are listed. Our definition of 'ingredient' in paragraph 10 allows for changes in ingredients during processing and would require listing of ingredients still present 'in part or wholly'. The ingredients of other foods can change during manufacture in much the same way as the ingredients of alcoholic drinks and it would be a logical progression for the headings of all ingredients lists to take this into account. We deal with ingredients list headings for other foods in paragraph 58.

22.   The remaining major argument submitted against ingredient listing for alcoholic drinks was that there was no real consumer demand, that any demand there was existed only as part of a general movement in favour of ingredient listing and that the consumer was not interested in the ingredients of alcoholic drinks but in the alcohol content and the flavour. Many consumers never saw the label of a bottle as they bought drinks by the glass in a bar or club and to require such information on the label would not, therefore, benefit or inform a significant proportion of consumers. We do not consider these arguments outweigh the principles indicated above and therefore *recommend* that alcoholic drinks should not be exempt from any requirement to list ingredients. We are aware that as yet no other country requires full ingredient listing of all alcoholic drinks but this may well change in the next few years. This subject has been under consideration for some time in the USA. We do not believe therefore that we are recommending a measure which is out of line with general international developments.

23.   *Bread and flour, flour confectionery, biscuits.* The main problems for

these products which it has been said would arise if ingredient listing were to be required are the length of the ingredients lists, particularly for flour confectionery, the inequity of treatment for prepacked goods if non-prepacked continued to be exempt and the problems that would arise for the great numbers of small bakers and confectioners producing their own limited range of prepacked goods.

24. Bread and flour form an important part of the diet and there is considerable consumer interest in their ingredients. We did not recommend ingredient listing for bread or flour in our Second Report on Bread and Flour[9] because the extension of this provision to a single group of exempt foods would have been inequitable. In the context of a general review we now see no argument against the provision of this information for these staple foods.

25. Flour confectionery and biscuits raise different problems from those of bread. Both tend to be complex foods with a large number of ingredients. We have been told, for example, that a French jam sandwich could have thirty-one ingredients and that as cakes are usually eaten for pleasure only there is little benefit to the consumer in being given a detailed list of ingredients. With biscuits the arguments are similar, the problem of boxes of mixed biscuits being given as a further example of difficulty. We do not, however, accept these arguments. These problems could be met by the provision of suitable generic terms and the provisions which may be made for using only the name of a compound ingredient instead of all its constituents (this is discussed in paragraphs 59-61). We believe that the problems we have outlined are greatly reduced in this way and the consumer will receive more information than at present. Some flour confectionery and biscuit manufacturers already list ingredients and this strengthens our view that there are no major difficulties.

26. The question of inequity of treatment between prepacked and non-prepacked is likely to be a continuing problem. It already exists in the field of meat products, particularly meat pies and sausages and it is difficult to see how it can be overcome completely. We accept the argument that the consumer buying non-prepacked bread has as much right as the one buying prepacked bread to know the ingredients but can see major problems in requiring ingredient listing of non-prepacked foods.

27. Regarding the problem of the small master baker, we have been told that many such bakers vary recipes, using a variety of doughs made up from different ingredients and that this and the practice of estimating some ingredients by experience make accurate ingredient listing difficult. This problem is in many ways similar to that of non-prepacked food and is also of concern to other sectors of the food industry. We believe however that the principle of ingredient listing for these foods is right.

---

[9]Food Standards Committee Second Report on Bread and Flour: FSC/REP/61: HMSO 1974

28.   We have not dealt in this Report with the particular problems associated with small businesses or the labelling of non-prepacked foods since priority has been given only to those aspects of labelling dealt with in the draft directive on food labelling. The draft directive leaves both subjects to be dealt with under national legislation. We shall therefore deal with these in a later report.

29.   *Chocolate confectionery, cocoa and chocolate products.* Chocolate confectionery is exempt from a requirement to declare ingredients under the 1970 Labelling of Food Regulations. Cocoa and chocolate products, whilst also being exempt, are required by the Cocoa and Chocolate Products Regulations 1976[10] to declare particular ingredients, for example, the minimum percentage of cocoa solids. A full list of ingredients would provide more useful information to consumers than a partial declaration and we see no reason why all the ingredients should not be listed.

30.   We have been told that there may be difficulties in listing the ingredients of boxes of assorted chocolates in the correct order since the contents could vary according to availability. We believe that most of these problems could be overcome by the use of generic terms but there may be a need to consider the use of a phrase such as 'These chocolates are made from . . . . . .'. We *recommend* accordingly. Similar problems could also arise with selections which contain a number of separate individual products normally sold separately such as chocolate bars. For these products we *recommend* that ingredients need not be declared on the outer wrapper provided the individual items are declared and the ingredients are listed on each individual item of confectionery within the box. This does not detract from the principle of no exemption from ingredient listing.

31.   *Sugar confectionery.* These products should be treated in the same way as chocolate confectionery and cocoa and chocolate products. We do not accept the argument that the consumer is not interested in the ingredients.

32.   *Ice-cream (including dairy ice-cream and milk ice), Parev or Kosher ice.* We do not believe that there is any longer a case for the exemption of these products. The larger manufacturers already accept this and seek merely to ensure that suitable generic terms are available. Smaller manufacturers face greater problems since availability of some ingredients may alter quickly. Label changes to keep pace with these could be expensive and wasteful. We think that some of the problems of the small manufacturer/retailer are similar to those of the master baker. We do not think that these problems outweigh the obligation on those producing prepacked foods of this type to acquaint consumers with the ingredients used.

33.   *Butter and cheese (not including processed cheese and cheese spread).* Butter is exempt from ingredient declaration under the 1970 Labelling of Food

---

[10]England and Wales SI 1976 No. 541
    Scotland SI 1976 No. 914 (S 78)
    Northern Ireland SR (NI) 1976 No. 183

Regulations and also under the EEC draft directive on food labelling, provided no ingredient has been added other than lactic products, enzymes and micro-organism cultures essential to manufacture. We consider that details of the ingredients of this important staple food should be available. It is doubtful whether consumers are aware that ingredients such as colour are often used and a declaration of ingredients would accordingly be of interest to consumers. We are not aware of any special problems likely to be encountered in listing all ingredients.

34. Cheese other than processed cheese or cheese spread is exempt under the 1970 Labelling of Food Regulations and would also be exempt under the terms of the EEC draft directive on food labelling provided no ingredient other than salt has been added. We consider that the same arguments apply as for other staple items of the diet. We think that the consumer should be provided with a full list of ingredients.

35. *Fermented milk.* Fermented milk, which we understand to include yogurt, is exempted from ingredient listing under Article 6 of the EEC draft directive on food labelling in the same way as butter (paragraph 33). We can see no justification for such exemption.

36. *Condensed milk and dried milk.* Special labelling of both these products is already required[11]. We do not however consider that exemption from ingredient listing should continue, there being no special case for treating these foods exceptionally. Some difficulties could occur because of seasonal fluctuations in the composition of the major ingredient, milk, where it is sometimes necessary to add stabilising salts to adjust the salt balance. However, this is true of other foods, and we make further reference to the possible ways of overcoming such problems in paragraphs 55-57.

37. *Coffee and chicory mixtures including French coffee: coffee with fig flavour or fig seasoning, including Viennese coffee.* It was suggested to us that where all the ingredients of a food appear in the name, the food should not be required also to bear a list of ingredients. We have already expressed our views on this subject in paragraph 11. We believe that the consumer is entitled to information about ingredients other than coffee in these products.

38. *Artificial sweetening tablets.* Artificial sweetening tablets may contain ingredients other than the sweetener saccharin, sodium saccharin, or calcium saccharin. Sodium bicarbonate, for instance, is often present to help the tablet

---

[11] (a) The Condensed Milk Regulations
England and Wales SI 1959 No. 1098
Scotland SI 1959 No. 1115 (S 65)
Northern Ireland SR and O (NI)
1961 No. 31

    (b) The Dried Milk Regulations
England and Wales SI 1965 No. 363
Scotland SI 1965 No. 1007 (S 35)
Northern Ireland SR and O (NI)
1965 No. 44

    (c) The Condensed Milk and Dried Milk
Regulations
England and Wales SI 1977 No. 928
Scotland SI 1977 No. 1027 (S 80)
Northern Ireland SR (NI) 1977 No. 196

dissolve and other substances are present as carriers for the sweetener. We believe the consumer should be given information about these substances.

39. *Curry Powder*. In paragraph 8 of our 1970 Report on the Pre-1955 Compositional Orders it was recommended that curry powder should no longer be exempt from ingredient listing. We confirm this view. We discuss other recommendations made in that Report in relation to generic terms for curry powder in paragraph 52 below.

40. *Gelatine*. The principal addition to gelatine is sulphur dioxide, the declaration of which, as permitted preservative, can reasonably be required. Where no such addition is made, gelatine can be regarded as a single ingredient food and as such a declaration of ingredients would not be appropriate.

41. *'Any meal'*. This, with fresh fruit and vegetables below, is the only present exemption for which, in our view, there is sufficient justification for a continuation. 'Meal' is defined in Regulation 2 (1) of the 1970 Labelling of Food Regulations as 'any collection of two or more foods of distinctly different kinds which is suitable for consumption as a complete meal and is packed as a meal in a container bearing a label on which there appears in a conspicuous position a clear and legible statement to the effect that it is a complete meal and which at the time of sale is ready for consumption without cooking, heating or other preparation . . .' The exemption is intended to apply to packed lunches, etc. supplied by hotels, guest houses, cafes, caterers, etc. A requirement to list all the ingredients would in our view be impracticable. The individual components of these meals are likely to vary from day to day and probably also during the day as particular foods are used up. It would be virtually impossible for those supplying these meals to be aware of the constituents of each component food and it would be similarly impossible for any ingredient list to reflect accurately all the changes all the time. A lengthy list of ingredients would in our view be of little information to the consumer, who will be much more interested in the component foods. We therefore *recommend* that 'any meal', as at present defined in the 1970 Labelling of Food Regulations, remains totally exempt from the need for a declaration of ingredients when sold to residents of hotels, guest houses, etc. We further *recommend* that other sales of such meals continue to be exempt provided the component foods are listed on a ticket or notice. A requirement to list the component foods making up the meal would, in our view, be fairly easy to comply with and at the same time would provide consumers with the necessary information.

42. *Fresh fruit and vegetables*. Exemption for these foods is provided under both the 1970 Labelling of Food Regulations and the EEC draft directive on food labelling. Having examined the difficulties involved, we *recommend* that prepacked fresh fruit and vegetables should remain exempt from ingredient listing provided that for mixed fruit and mixed vegetables the appropriate designation or common or usual name identifies the individual items. Many packs of fresh fruit and vegetables will, of course, contain only a single type of

fruit or vegetable and are single ingredient foods and as such need not be required to list the ingredient.

43. *Specified sugar products.* These products are exempt from Part II of the 1970 Labelling of Food Regulations by virtue of Regulation 4 (3). Most of them are essentially single ingredient foods but, where not, certain declarations of particular ingredients are required by compositional regulations[12]. We can however see no reason for such selectivity: a full list of ingredients will be of more use to the consumer.

44. *Honey.* Although honey is specifically excluded from Part II of the 1970 Labelling of Food Regulations, it is for legislative[13] and all practical purposes a single ingredient food. A specific exemption from ingredient listing is therefore inappropriate and unnecessary.

45. *Vinegar.* Article 6.1a (a) of the EEC draft directive on food labelling exempts 'fermented vinegars derived exclusively from a single basic product'. We can see no justification for such a specific exemption.

46. *Small containers.* Some labels on small containers will not be sufficiently large to accommodate all the statutory information. Regulation 6 (4) of the 1970 Labelling of Food Regulations allows containers whose greatest dimension does not exceed 5 cm to omit the ingredients list if space on the label is insufficient. Under Article 10 of the EEC draft directive on food labelling, at the discretion of Member States, small containers whose largest surface measures less than 10 square cm need not bear an ingredients list. We are not generally in favour of an exemption from ingredient listing for small containers. Where there is a minimum type size as in the 1970 Labelling of Food Regulations a stage may be reached where it is not possible to get all the statutory information on the label. But where, as in the EEC draft directive on food labelling, no such minimum type size is set this does not apply. We have seen labels, for instance on individually wrapped sweets, where the ingredients list is in very small but still legible print. Only if a minimum type size were specified in the draft directive could we support the proposed small container exemption.

---

[12]The Specified Sugar Products Regulations
England and Wales SI 1976 No. 509
Scotland SI 1976 No. 946 (S 82)
Northern Ireland SR (NI) 1976 No. 165

[13]The Honey Regulations
England and Wales SI 1976 No. 1832
Scotland SI 1976 No. 1818 (S 143)
Northern Ireland SR (NI) 1976 No. 387

Generic Terms

47. *General.* Our recommendation in paragraph 10 that there should no longer be any exemptions from ingredients listing is made in conjunction with the availability of a range of suitable generic terms which can obviate many of the difficulties referred to above. Generic terms can also be of great help to the consumer in understanding the information presented on food labels. In some circumstances a simple straightforward term will convey more than a long and complicated chemical name: 'preservative' for instance will be more understandable than 'methyl 4-hydroxybenzoate'. At the same time, however, we are concerned that any generic terms used should not be too widely drawn so that little real information is conveyed when the term is used in an ingredients list. We therefore *recommend* that, where appropriate, generic terms should be available for use by manufacturers to help overcome real labelling difficulties: the coverage of any generic terms allowed should be closely defined and the terms used should be understandable to consumers.

48. We have noted that in the EEC draft directive on food labelling most classes of food additives would be required to be declared in an ingredients list as a generic term followed by the specific name or EEC number. If this requirement is adopted by Member States, manufacturers would no longer have the freedom they have currently in the U.K. to use a generic term on its own in an ingredients list. Each additive present would have to be identified precisely and this could present difficulties in labelling. We understand that this requirement arises from evidence which suggests that some food additives might cause hypersensitive or allergenic reactions in certain individuals and there is a consequent need to identify specifically all these substances when used in food. We cannot agree with this approach. Some people are hypersensitive or allergic to certain foods and ingredients of foods just as much as to certain food additives but serious reactions are experienced by only a very small minority. If a food additive gives rise to widespread hypersensitivity problems, the proper course of action would seem to us to be to ban its use on medical grounds rather than to ensure it is always specifically declared on labels so that it can be avoided by the informed consumer. We cannot recommend the adoption of the proposed EEC labelling requirement for additives. The use of food colours is one of the main areas in this respect. It is currently being examined by the Food Additives and Contaminants Committee (FACC) and the Toxicity Sub-Committee of the Chief Medical Officer's Committee on Medical Aspects of Chemicals in Food and the Environment. Although we have expressed our views on additive labelling above, these are necessarily subject to the wider considerations which the FACC and the Toxicity Sub-Committee will have in mind.

49. In the light of our views on the value of generic terms in paragraph 47 above, we have examined all the terms at present permitted by the 1970 Labelling of Food Regulations and those listed in Annexes I and II to the EEC draft directive on food labelling. At the same time we have also considered those generic terms recommended by us in previous reports (referred to in paragraph 4) together with suggestions for new terms made by interested

17

parties, including some terms needed for foods likely to be required to list ingredients for the first time. We examined each generic term to make sure it would be useful and readily understood by the consumer. Our recommendations are set out in paragraph 52.

50. *1970 Labelling of Food Regulations.* The following generic terms are at present permitted by paragraphs 1-3 of Schedule 2 to the 1970 Labelling of Food Regulations to be used to describe an ingredient in place of an appropriate designation:—

   1. 'Oil' or 'Fat' 'Shortening' (whether or not qualified as appropriate by the adjectives 'edible', 'vegetable' or 'animal' or any combination thereof)
   2. 'Emulsifying salts'
   3. 'Edible starch' or 'Food starch' or 'Starch'
   4. 'Imitation cream'
   5. 'Fish'
   6. 'Cheese'
   7. 'Fruit acids'
   8. 'Vine fruits'
   9. 'Vinegar'
   10. 'Spices' or 'Mixed spices'
   11. 'Herbs' or 'Mixed herbs'
   12. 'Edible gums'
   13. 'Meat'
   14. 'Other meat'
   15. 'Cereal binder'
   16. 'Sugar'
   17. 'Other fruit'
   18. 'Nuts'
   19. 'Honey'

Food Additives

   1. 'Flavourings'
   2. 'Permitted preservative'
   3. 'Permitted antioxidant'
   4. 'Permitted colour'
   5. 'Permitted emulsifier'
   6. 'Permitted stabiliser'
   7. 'Permitted solvent'

'Permitted' may be omitted from any of the generic terms for additives. The scope (i.e. coverage) of all the generic terms in the 1970 Regulations is set out in Regulation 2(1) for additives and Schedule 2, paragraph 1, for the remainder.

51. *EEC Draft Directive on Food Labelling.* Generic terms permitted or required are set out in Annexes I and II of the draft directive. These are by no

means comprehensive lists of the generic terms likely to be incorporated in future U.K. legislation since it is proposed that under national legislation other terms will be allowed for specified foods. We have not therefore specifically included in this Report a list of the generic terms in the draft directive although we have referred to each one as appropriate in paragraphs 52-54.

52. *Recommended generic terms (other than for food additives).* We *recommend* that the following revised list of generic terms appears in any new labelling regulations for use in ingredients lists: restriction of some terms for use only with particular foods is indicated. This list incorporates certain of the proposed terms in the EEC draft directive on food labelling, those terms recommended by us in other reports and some of those suggested by interested parties. We have commented on each term as appropriate. Generic terms rejected by us are set out in paragraph 54.

Term	Coverage	Comment
1. 'Cereal adjuncts'	For *beer* only: all unmalted cereals and all other edible starchy materials.	A new generic term: as recommended in paragraph 156 of our Report on Beer.
2. 'Cereal flakes'	Any flaked or crushed cereal.	A new generic term.
3. 'Cheese'	All types of cheese or mixtures of cheeses other than processed cheese and cheese spread provided that the name and presentation of the food does not refer to a specific type of cheese.	As in the EEC draft directive on food labelling.
4. 'Cheese cultures'	For *cheese* only: micro-organisms used as a starter characteristic of the particular cheese.	A new generic term.
5. 'Crumbs' or 'Rusks' as appropriate	All types of crumbed baked cereal products.	Bread crumbs and rusks are exempt from a declaration of their constituents when forming an ingredient of another food by virtue of Part III of Schedule 2 to the 1970 Labelling of Food Regulations. Both terms are listed in the draft labelling directive.
6. 'Cocoa butter'	Press, expeller or refined cocoa butter.	A new generic term: as in the draft labelling directive.
7. 'Dextrose'	Anhydrous dextrose and dextrose monohydrate.	A new generic term: as in the draft labelling directive.
8. 'Fish'	All species of fish provided that the name and presentation of the food does not refer to any species of fish.	As in the draft labelling directive.

20

Term	Coverage	Comment
9. 'Other fish'	Any kind of fish other than a fish named in the appropriate designation.	A new generic term. A term similar in scope and usage to 'other meat' would seem justified.
10. 'Gum base'	All types of gum used in the manufacture of chewing gum.	A new generic term: as in the draft labelling directive.
11. 'Herbs' or 'Mixed herbs'	When not exceeding 2% by weight of another food.	A 1% weight limit is specified in the 1970 Labelling of Food Regulations. In our Report on the Pre-1955 Compositional Orders it was recommended that the existing UK weight limit of 1% be waived for herbs and spices used as ingredients of curry powder. In the light of a general requirement for detailed ingredient listing for all foods we can no longer recommend such an exception.
12. 'Honey'	All types of honey when forming an ingredient of some other food.	As in the 1970 Labelling of Food Regulations.
13. 'Hops'	For *beer* only: powdered hops, hop extracts and whole hops (but excluding isomerized hop extracts or hop oils).	A new generic term: as recommended in paragraph 156 of our Report on Beer.
14. 'Hydrolysed vegetable protein'	Substantially or completely hydrolysed vegetable proteins prepared from vegetable matter with a minimum crude protein content of 50% calculated on a dry basis.	A new generic term.

Term	Coverage	Comment
15. 'Imitation cream'	Imitation cream.	As in the 1970 Labelling of Food Regulations. The composition of imitation cream is to some extent laid down in Section 47 of the Food and Drugs Act 1955.
16. 'Jam'	Jam.	Two new generic terms. We referred to the need to differentiate between the use of 'jam' and 'bakery jam' in our Report on the EEC Draft Directive on Fruit Jams, Jellies and Marmalades and Chestnut Purée[14].
17. 'Bakery jam'	Bakery jam.	
18. 'Meat'	Any kind of meat including permitted offal when an ingredient of a sausage, meat pie, meat pudding, sausage roll, vol-au-vent, faggot, hamburger, rissole, croquette, meat ball or haggis, except when the appropriate designation or common or usual name includes the name of a kind of meat and the meat content does not consist wholly of that kind of meat.	As in the 1970 Labelling of Food Regulations.
19. 'Other meat'	Any kind of meat including permitted offal when an ingredient of a sausage, meat pie, meat pudding, sausage roll, vol-au-vent, faggot, hamburger, rissole, croquette or meat ball, other than a meat named in the appropriate designation or common or usual name.	As in the 1970 Labelling of Food Regulations.

[14]Food Standards Committee Report on the EEC Draft Directive on Fruit Jams, Jellies and Marmalades and Chestnut Purèe: FSC/REP/66: MAFF 1976

Term	Coverage	Comment
20. 'Nuts'	Nuts when forming an ingredient (a) of a mixture of nuts and vine fruit packed in net amounts not exceeding 50 g; or (b) of some other food, but not exceeding 1% by weight of such food.	As in the 1970 Labelling of Food Regulations.
21. 'Offal'	Offal other than permitted offal when forming an ingredient of any *cooked* meat product (The Offals in Meat Products Order 1953[15] prohibits the use of offal other than permitted offal in the composition or preparation of any *uncooked* open meat product).	A new generic term: as recommended in paragraphs 39 and 43 of our Report on Offals in Meat Products.
22. 'Oil' or 'Fat' qualified as appropriate by 'animal', 'vegetable', 'fish', or 'whale' ('animal' includes birds)	Fatty oils or fats whether hydrogenated or not.	A declaration of the origin of the oil or fat used as an ingredient is not required by the 1970 Labelling of Food Regulations. The requirements of the draft labelling directive remain to be clarified. With the increasing public interest in the use of these ingredients we consider that information about the raw material source should now be required. A declaration in the broad terms we have recommended should provide the consumer with useful information yet at the same time still allow manufacturers a degree of flexibility. We have recommended a separate declaration of whale products since it would be

[15]SI 1953 No. 246 (Applies to England and Wales, Scotland and Northern Ireland)

Term	Coverage	Comment
22. 'Oil' or 'Fat' etc (continued)		inappropriate for these to be described either as 'fish' or 'animal'. We considered the need for the provision of other information about these ingredients. A declaration of the presence of dairy fats, for instance, would be useful to some consumers. However, dairy fats such as butter are usually so described in ingredients lists and therefore we would not wish to see such a distinction being required. We would however like to see manufacturers label their products accordingly where this was considered helpful to the consumer. We also considered the need to refer to hydrogenation where this had taken place. To single out only one aspect of fats and oils manufacture however could be misleading. 'Shortening' (at present allowed as a generic term by the 1970 Labelling of Food Regulations) is not recommended since 'fat' or 'oil' suitably qualified is considered sufficient. We will deal with the whole subject of polyunsaturated/saturated fatty acid labelling in a later Report.
23. 'Other fruit'	Any two or more kinds of fruit when less than 50% by weight of the fruit content of a preserve containing three or more kinds of fruit.	As in the 1970 Labelling of Food Regulations. This term is currently being considered in discussions on the EEC draft directive on fruit jams, jellies, marmalades and chestnut purée.

Term	Coverage	Comment
24. 'Spices' or 'Mixed spices'	When not exceeding 2% by weight of another food.	See our comments under 'Herbs' or 'Mixed herbs'.
25. 'Starch'	Native, enzymatically and physically modified starch.	The present generic term 'starch' in the 1970 Labelling of Food Regulations needs to be redefined to distinguish between starches modified by physical or enzymatic and chemical means. The draft labelling directive refers to 'starch' and 'chemically modified starch'.
26. 'Modified starch'	Starch modified by chemical means.	
27. 'Sugar'	Any form of the product consisting principally of sucrose and usually known, with or without qualification, as sugar.	As in the 1970 Labelling of Food Regulations and broadly in line with the draft labelling directive.
28 'Sugar adjuncts'	For *beer* only: all sugars used (including primings).	A new generic term: as recommended in paragraph 156 of our Report on Beer.
29. 'Vine fruits'	Muscatels, raisins, sultanas and currants.	As in the 1970 Labelling of Food Regulations.
30. 'Vinegar'	Any kind of vinegar.	As in the 1970 Labelling of Food Regulations.
31. 'Yogurt cultures'	For *yogurt* only: lactic acid producing bacteria.	A new generic term as recommended in paragraph 46 of our Report on Yogurt; the term may not be necessary under the draft labelling directive which exempts fermented milk from ingredient listing (see paragraph 5).

53. *Recommended generic terms for food additives.* We *recommend* that the following generic terms for food additives appear in any new labelling regulations.

Term	Comment
1. 'Acid'	New generic terms. 'Acid' should replace 'fruit acid' in the 1970 Labelling of Food Regulations. It is preferable to 'food acid' which is likely to be included in the draft labelling directive. All three terms are preferable to 'pH regulator' suggested in representations.
2. 'Alkali'	
3. 'Buffer salt'	
4. 'Anti-caking agent'	As in the draft labelling directive: preferred to 'free-flow agent', 'edible excipient' or 'edible diluent' as have been suggested.
5. 'Anti-foaming agent'	As in the draft labelling directive.
6. 'Antioxidant'	As in the 1970 Labelling of Food Regulations and the draft labelling directive.
7. 'Colour'	As in the 1970 Labelling of Food Regulations and the draft labelling directive.
8. 'Emulsifier'	As in the 1970 Labelling of Food Regulations and the draft labelling directive. Coverage, as in the Emulsifiers and Stabilisers in Food Regulations 1975[16], includes edible gums.
9. 'Emulsifying salts'	As in the Cheese Regulations 1970 as amended[17], namely the ammonium, sodium, potassium or calcium salts of citric and orthophosphoric acid; the sodium, potassium or calcium salts of diphosphoric acid; pentasodium triphosphate; pentapotassium triphosphate; ammonium, sodium, potassium and calcium polyphosphate; the sodium, potassium or potassium sodium salts of tartaric acid insofar as their use is permitted by the Miscellaneous Additives in Food Regulations 1974,

---

[16]England and Wales SI 1975 No. 1486 as amended by SI 1976 No. 1886
Scotland SI 1975 No. 1597 (S 228) as amended by SI 1976 No. 1911 (S 157)
Northern Ireland SR (NI) 1975 No. 278 as amended by SR (NI) 1976 No. 367

[17]England and Wales SI 1970 No. 94 as amended by SI 1974 No. 1122 and the Colouring Matter in Food Regulations SI 1976 No. 2086
Scotland SI 1970 No. 108 (S 4) as amended by SI 1974 No. 1337 (S 115) and SI 1976 No. 2232 (S 184)
Northern Ireland SR & O (NI) 1970 No. 14 as amended by SR (NI) 1974 No. 177 & SR (NI) 1976 No. 382

Term	Comment
9. 'Emulsifying salts' (continued)	as amended[18]. This term would be permitted only for *processed cheese* and *processed cheese products.*
10. 'Enzymes'	A new generic term for enzymes still present (active or inactive) in the finished product.
11. 'Flavour'	'Flavourings' are referred to in the 1970 Labelling of Food Regulations. We prefer 'flavour' to be consistent with 'colour'.
12. 'Maturing agents'	A new generic term for *flour* only which is more appropriate than 'flour improvers' in the draft labelling directive and 'bleaching agent', 'flour conditioning agent' or 'improver' as have been suggested since 'maturing' includes both bleaching and conditioning.
13. 'Glazing agent'	As in the draft labelling directive.
14. 'Liquid freezant'	Already permitted by Regulation 18A[19] of the 1970 Labelling of Food Regulations for use on the labels of foods frozen with dichlorodifluoromethane.
15. 'Preservative'	As in the 1970 Labelling of Food Regulations and the draft labelling directive.
16. 'Raising agent'	As in the draft labelling directive: for *bread* and *flour confectionery* only. More understandable than 'aerating agent'.
17. 'Release agent'	A new generic term: preferable to 'tin release agent' as suggested in representations.
18. 'Solvent'	As in the 1970 Labelling of Food Regulations.
19. 'Stabiliser'	As in the 1970 Labelling of Food Regulations and the draft labelling directive. Coverage, as in the

[18]England and Wales SI 1974 No. 1121 as amended by SI 1975 No. 1485
Scotland SI 1974 No. 1338 (S 116) as amended by SI 1975 No. 1596 (S 227)
Northern Ireland SR (NI) 1974 No. 196 as amended by SR (NI) 1975 No. 275

[19]The text of Regulation 18A of the 1970 Labelling of Food Regulations may be found in Regulation 3 of the Miscellaneous Additives in Food (Amendment) Regulations 1975 (England and Wales 1975 No. 1485;
Scotland SI 1975 No. 1596 (S 227);
Northern Ireland SR & O (NI) 1975 No. 275

Term	Comment
19. 'Stabiliser' (continued)	Emulsifiers and Stabilisers in Food Regulations 1975, includes edible gums.
20. 'Stabilising salts'	A new generic term to cover the bicarbonates, citrates and phosphates of sodium and potassium and calcium chloride as in the Condensed Milk and Dried Milk Regulations 1977. The term should be permitted for milk products only, the salts being used to adjust the salt balance of the milk, which may vary seasonally before processing into products such as condensed milk so as to achieve a consistent product (see also our comments in paragraphs 55-57).
21. 'Yeast nutrients'	A new generic term: preferable to 'yeast foods' or 'dough conditioners' as suggested in representations.

Under the 1970 Labelling of Food Regulations (Schedule 2, paragraph 3) the use of the word 'permitted' to accompany generic terms for additives is optional. A permitted preservative may therefore be declared as either 'permitted preservative' or 'preservative'. We consider that to achieve a more uniform declaration of ingredients, which will consequently be easier for the consumer to understand, the optional use of the word 'permitted' should no longer be allowed. Generic terms for additives should now be as we have recommended above.

54.   *Generic terms rejected.* In recommending a revised list of generic terms for future legislation we examined a number of terms, either already in legislation, proposed by the EEC draft directive on food labelling, or suggested by interested parties which we consider did not meet the criteria set out in paragraph 47. The generic terms we have rejected are as follows:—

(a)   *Aromatic seeds.* This term was recommended in paragraph 8 of our Report on The Pre-1955 Compositional Orders. In considering the representations received, however, we concluded that the generic terms 'herbs' and 'spices' as recommended in paragraph 52 are sufficient to deal with any difficulties in ingredient listing.

(b)   *Caseinates.* This term is listed in the EEC draft directive on food labelling. We consider that its use is unnecessary: we know of no problems in ingredient listing which would make the term necessary and it is too vague to be helpful to consumers.

(c)   *Cereal binder.* This term is at present permitted by the 1970 Labelling of Food Regulations (see paragraph 50). We are concerned that its scope is too wide to provide useful information to the consumer, particularly since as defined it covers both non-leguminous and leguminous material thus permitting any vegetable binder used as an ingredient to be described by this term. We are sure that this was not the intention when the term was first introduced into legislation. Of particular concern to us was the inclusion of 'soya flour and soya starch and groundnut flour and groundnut lipoprotein' which could not in our view be appropriately described as 'cereal binder'. We understand that one sector of the food industry currently using the term on their labels could quite easily declare the specific binder used without any problems. With this in mind and because 'starch', 'cereal flakes' and 'crumbs' or 'rusks' are recommended as generic terms we can see no reason for the continued use of the term 'cereal binder'.

(d) *Cheese spread/processed cheese.* We consider that existing generic terms adequately deal with any difficulties in listing the constituents of these two foods when ingredients of another food.

(e) *Citrus peel.* We know of no special difficulties which would justify the use of this term.

(f) *Cured meat.* We were asked to consider the use of this term to describe the cured meat component of comminuted spreadable meat products. We consider that if the meat used is not 'ham', ie not from the hind leg of the pig, it should be described by its appropriate designation, ie cured pork.

(g) *Fruit acid.* This term is at present permitted under the 1970 Labelling of Food Regulations (see paragraph 50). We have recommended in paragraph 53 that it should more suitably be replaced by the generic term 'acid'.

(h) *Fruits as available/mixed fruits.* The present permitted generic term 'other fruit' (see paragraph 50) would seem to deal adequately with the difficulties envisaged by those suggesting these terms.

(j) *Fruit juices.* We can see no justification for such a broad term: the individual fruit juices used in a food should always be specifically identified.

(k) *Pastry.* This term could be used to cover far too wide a range of individual constituents. With pie products it might however be more helpful to the consumer if the pastry constituents were listed separately from the filling.

(l) *Poultry meat.* This is listed in the EEC draft directive on food labelling. The generic term 'meat' as recommended is sufficient and there is little need for a separate term for meat derived from poultry.

(m) *Shortening.* This is at present allowed as an alternative to the generic terms 'fat' or 'oil' in the 1970 Labelling of Food Regulations (see paragraph 50). Shortening is a compound food usually consisting of a blend of oils and fats, whether hydrogenated or not, possibly together with emulsifiers. We consider that a generic term would be inappropriate to describe this ingredient and we have recommended accordingly in paragraph 52.

29

(n)   *Textured.* This term was suggested for use with novel protein foods used as ingredients to cover all methods of texturing including spinning. The use of such an adjective is in our view inappropriate to a list of generic terms: the specific process used for novel protein foods should be given as part of the appropriate designation of the ingredient as recommended in paragraph 97 of our Report on Novel Protein Foods[20].

(p)   *Vegetable protein.* We were asked by interested parties to consider the generic term 'vegetable protein' to cover the use of protein extenders in sausages. We understand however that any need for this and similar terms is likely to be covered by proposals for regulations on novel protein foods.

FOOD ADDITIVES

(q)   *Aerating agent.* This term was proposed for use in the ingredients lists of bread, should bread no longer be exempt. We consider that 'raising agent' as recommended in paragraph 53 is a more informative term.

(r)   *Acidity regulator/pH regulator.* The former term is listed in the EEC draft directive on food labelling. The recommended terms 'acid', 'alkali' and 'buffer salt' are more appropriate.

(s)   *Artificial sweetener.* This term is listed in the EEC draft directive on food labelling. Since at the present time only one artificial sweetener is permitted in the UK a generic term is unnecessary.

(t)   *Edible excipient/edible diluent/free-flow agent.* 'Anti-caking agent' (as listed in the EEC draft directive on food labelling and recommended in paragraph 53) is more understandable than any of these terms.

(u)   *Flavour enhancer/flavour modifier.* The latter is listed in the EEC draft directive on food labelling. Both terms are likely to cover far too wide a range of substances to be at all informative.

(v)   *Flour improvers/maturing agent/improver.* The first is listed in the EEC draft directive on food labelling. Our recommendation of 'maturing agent' in paragraph 53 is more appropriate.

(w)   *Foaming agent.* Since there are many natural substances regarded as foods which perform this function as well as additives the use of this generic term is unnecessary.

(x)   *Gelling agent.* This term is listed in the EEC draft directive on food labelling. We doubt whether there are sufficient of these substances available to warrant a separate generic term.

(y)   *Humectant.* We can see little need for this term and doubt whether it would be readily understood by consumers.

(z)   *Mineral hydrocarbons.* These substances are not generally allowed in food but where they are specifically permitted they should be declared.

(aa) *Packaging gas.* Only a few such gases are used and each can be declared specifically.

---

[20]Food Standards Committee Report on Novel Protein Foods: FSC/REP/62: HMSO 1974

(ab) *Permitted miscellaneous additive.* This term is too imprecise and covers far too many substances to be at all helpful.

(ac) *Sequestrant.* We do not believe that the average consumer would understand the meaning of this term.

(ad) *Thickening agent/thickener.* The latter term is listed in the EEC draft directive on food labelling. The coverage of both terms is likely to be too wide to be very helpful to the consumer.

(ae) *Tin release agent.* 'Release agent' as recommended in paragraph 53 is preferable.

(af) *Yeast foods/dough conditioners.* 'Yeast nutrients' as recommended in paragraph 53 is a more appropriate and understandable term.

55.   *Foods subject to seasonal or other variations.* We referred in paragraphs 13, 17 and 36 to some of the difficulties occurring where an ingredient such as milk will vary in composition at certain times of the year and it is necessary at those times to adjust the composition to achieve a consistent product. Ingredient lists will for this reason need to be changed at intervals to take account of the fluctuations in the main ingredient. This is a particular problem for products such as condensed milk which will, under our proposals, have to declare its ingredients for the first time.

56.   Difficulties can also occur, but in different ways, with some other foods. Bread, for instance, may need to have preservative added during the warmer summer months. Canned fruits and vegetables may need the addition of certain salts depending upon the hardness of the water supply.

57.   We would not wish our proposals to result in costly label changes in relation to only minor ingredients, and we will need to examine the difficulties presented. We therefore look to manufacturers to provide details of variations such as those referred to in paragraphs 55 and 56 so that suitable recommendations can be made.

HEADING TO INGREDIENTS LISTS

58.   In paragraph 21 we recommended that the term 'Ingredients used' head the ingredients lists of alcoholic drinks. We also mentioned that it would be a logical progression for this term to be used for the headings of all ingredients lists. We examined the use of such a term for all foods and we consider that not only is this more appropriate than 'Ingredients', covering as it does those instances where ingredients may be substantially changed in the final product, but also it is more informative to consumers. An ingredients list headed 'Ingredients used' will indicate precisely the ingredients used in the 'mixing bowl' but at the same time conveys the idea that these may have changed during the manufacturing process. This will of course already be appreciated by many consumers who do their own cooking. We *recommend* therefore that the term 'Ingredients used' head ingredients lists of all foods and drinks.

31

DECLARATION OF CONSTITUENTS OF INGREDIENTS

59. It is a requirement of the 1970 Labelling of Food Regulations (Regulation 5 (2) proviso (b)) that, with certain exceptions, where an ingredient is made from two or more constituents the appropriate designations of those constituents must be given in the ingredients list. The ingredients which are exempt from this requirement are listed in Part III of Schedule 2 to the 1970 Regulations: an appropriate designation of the ingredient can be given in place of the separate constituents.

60. A similar requirement to declare the constituents of ingredients is proposed under the EEC draft directive on food labelling. Exemption is however given to a compound ingredient (but not to any additives it contains) provided it forms less than 25% of the finished product and to foods already exempt from ingredient declaration under EEC regulations.

61. We accept that consumers should be given information about the constituents of ingredients in the same way as they are given information about the ingredients themselves. As a general principle therefore the constituents of ingredients should be declared. In listing all the constituents however there may be difficulties for manufacturers in that in some cases the ingredients list might become particularly long and complicated. The foods listed in Part III of Schedule 2 to the 1970 Labelling of Food Regulations are exempt from constituent listing either because they are at present exempt from ingredient listing or because the consumer is generally familiar with their composition. If our recommendations are accepted, the vast majority of foods will have ingredients declared on the label and exemption from constituent listing solely on the grounds of exemption from ingredient declaration would appear no longer to be justified. In this situation, however, there may be an argument for exemption of foods whose composition is fairly well known on the basis that information about the foods used as ingredients will be freely available on the labels of these foods when sold as such. Coupled with our wish to avoid wherever possible unnecessary costs for manufacturers (through the need to prepare lengthy and complicated ingredients lists), we *recommend* that the foods listed in Part III of Schedule 2 to the 1970 Labelling of Food Regulations should form the basis of any new list of exemptions from constituent listing. The provisions of the EEC draft directive on food labelling, if adopted, will also allow exemption in a similar way for a wider range of foods but under rather more limited circumstances.

SUMMARY OF CONCLUSIONS AND RECOMMENDATIONS

62. (1) *All prepacked foods and drinks* other than those consisting of a single ingredient and 'any meal' and 'prepacked fresh fruit and vegetables' (see below) should be required to bear a full list of ingredients. If suitable generic terms are available which obviate the need for repeated and costly switching of labels, many problems in listing ingredients can be overcome (paragraph 10).

(2) *'Ingredient'* should be defined along the lines of the current definition in the EEC draft directive on food labelling (paragraph 10).

32

(3) *Alcoholic drinks* should not be exempt from any requirement to list ingredients. The term 'Ingredients used' should head ingredients lists, indicating that the materials which were originally present do not necessarily remain in the final product (paragraphs 21 and 22).

(4) Most of the difficulties in listing the ingredients of boxes of assorted *chocolates* should be overcome by the use of generic terms but there may be a need to consider the use of a phrase such as 'These chocolates are made from . . . . . .'. Selections which contain a number of separate individual products normally sold separately such as chocolate bars should not be required to declare ingredients on the outer wrapper provided the individual items are declared and ingredients are listed on each item of confectionery within the box (paragraph 30).

(5) *'Any meal'* as at present defined in the 1970 Labelling of Food Regulations should remain totally exempt from the need for a declaration of ingredients when sold to residents of hotels, guest houses, etc. Other sales of such meals should continue to be exempt provided the component foods are listed on a ticket or notice (paragraph 41).

(6) *Prepacked fresh fruit and vegetables* should remain exempt from ingredient listing providing that in the case of mixed fruit and mixed vegetables the appropriate designation or common or usual name identifies the individual items (paragraph 42).

(7) Where appropriate, generic terms should be available for use by manufacturers to help overcome real labelling difficulties: the coverage of any generic terms allowed should be closely defined and the terms used should be understandable to consumers (paragraph 47).

(8) Revised lists of generic terms should appear in any new labelling regulations (paragraphs 52 and 53).

(9) The term 'Ingredients used' should head the ingredients lists of all foods and drinks (paragraph 58).

(10) The foods listed in Part III of Schedule 2 to the 1970 Labelling of Food Regulations should form the basis of any new list of exemptions from constituent listing (paragraph 61).

FSC/REP/69B   September 1977

REVIEW OF FOOD LABELLING PART II

EXEMPTIONS FROM INGREDIENT LISTING AND GENERIC TERMS

APPENDIX 1

LIST OF ORGANISATIONS AND INDIVIDUALS FROM WHOM EVIDENCE HAS BEEN RECEIVED

The list is identical with that on pages 1-4 of Appendix I to the Second Report on Food Labelling

APPENDIX 3

II

(Acts whose publication is not obligatory)

COUNCIL

COUNCIL DIRECTIVE

of 18 December 1978

on the approximation of the laws of the Member States relating to the labelling, presentation and advertising of foodstuffs for sale to the ultimate consumer

(79/112/EEC)

THE COUNCIL OF THE EUROPEAN COMMUNITIES,

Having regard to the Treaty establishing the European Economic Community, and in particular Articles 100 and 227 thereof,

Having regard to the proposal from the Commission[1],

Having regard to the opinion of the European Parliament [2],

Having regard to the opinion of the Economic and Social Committee [3],

Whereas differences which exist at present between the laws, regulations and administrative provisions of Member States on the labelling of foodstuffs impede the free circulation of these products and can lead to unequal conditions of competition;

Whereas, therefore, approximation of these laws would contribute to the smooth functioning of the common market;

Whereas the purpose of this Directive should be to enact Community rules of a general nature applicable horizontally to all foodstuffs put on the market;

Whereas rules of a specific nature which apply vertically only to particular foodstuffs should be laid down in provisions dealing with those products;

Whereas, moreover, the field of application of this Directive should be limited to foodstuffs intended for sale to the ultimate consumer, and the rules governing the labelling of products intended for subsequent processing or preparation should be fixed at a later stage;

Whereas the prime consideration for any rules on the labelling of foodstuffs should be the need to inform and protect the consumer;

Whereas, therefore, a list should be drawn up of all information which should in principle be included in the labelling of all foodstuffs;

Whereas, however, the horizontal nature of this Directive does not allow, at the initial stage, the inclusion in the compulsory indications of all the indications which must be added to the list applying in principle to the whole range of foodstuffs; whereas, during the second stage, Community provisions should be adopted, aimed at

---

[1] OJ No C 91, 22.4.1976, p.3.
[2] OJ No C 178, 2.8.1976, p.52.
[3] OJ No C 285, 2.12.1976, p.3.

1

supplementing the existing rules; whereas it would accordingly seem necessary to adopt as a matter of priority Community provisions regarding the indication of certain ingredients in the sales description or by indicating a quantity;

Whereas, furthermore, if in the absence of Community rules of a specific nature Member States should retain the right to lay down certain national provisions which may be added to the general provisions of this Directive, nevertheless these provisions should be subject to a Community procedure;

Whereas the said Community procedure may consist simply in informing the Commission and the Member States when the matter concerns the maintenance of national provisions that precede this Directive, but must be that of a Community Decision when a Member State wishes to enact new legislation;

Whereas provision should also be made for the Community legislator to derogate, in exceptional cases, from certain obligations that have been fixed generally;

Whereas the rules on labelling should also prohibit the use of information that would mislead the purchaser or attribute medicinal properties to foodstuffs; whereas, to be effective, this prohibition should also apply to the presentation and advertising of foodstuffs;

Whereas Member States should retain the right, depending on local conditions and circumstances, to lay down rules in respect of the labelling of foodstuffs sold in bulk; whereas, in such cases, information should nevertheless be provided for the consumer;

Whereas, with the aim of simplifying and accelerating the procedure, the Commission should be entrusted with the task of adopting implementing measures of a technical nature;

Whereas in all cases where the Council makes the Commission responsible for implementing rules laid down in respect of foodstuffs, provision should be made for a procedure instituting close cooperation between Member States and the Commission within the Standing Committee on Foodstuffs, set up by Decision 69/414/EEC[1];

Whereas foodstuffs in Greenland are manufactured and marketed under conditions fundamentally different from those prevailing in the other parts of the Community because of the island's general situation and, in particular, because of its commercial structures, low population, considerable area and special geographical situation,

HAS ADOPTED THIS DIRECTIVE:

Article 1

1. This Directive concerns the labelling of foodstuffs to be delivered as such to the ultimate consumer and certain aspects relating to the presentation and advertising thereof.

2. Without prejudice to the Community provisions to be adopted in this field, this Directive shall apply also to foodstuffs intended for supply to restaurants, hospitals, canteens and other similar mass caterers, in so far as the Member States shall so decide.

3. For the purpose of this Directive,

(a) 'labelling' shall mean any words, particulars, trade marks, brand name, pictorial matter or symbol relating to a foodstuff and placed on any packaging, document, notice, label, ring or collar accompanying or referring to such foodstuff;

(b) 'Pre-packaged foodstuff' shall mean any single item for presentation as such to the ultimate consumer, consisting of a foodstuff and the packaging into which it was put before being offered for sale, whether such packaging encloses the foodstuff completely or only partially, but in any case in such a way that the contents cannot be altered without opening or changing the packaging.

---

[1] OJ No L 291, 29.11.1969, p.9.

Article 2

1. The labelling and methods used must not:

(a) be such as could mislead the purchaser to a material degree, particularly:

  (i) as to the characteristics of the foodstuff and, in particular, as to its nature, identity, properties, composition, quantity, durability, origin or provenance, method of manufacture or production,

  (ii) by attributing to the foodstuff effects or properties which it does not possess,

  (iii) by suggesting that the foodstuff possesses special characteristics when in fact all similar foodstuffs possess such characteristics;

(b) subject to the provisions applicable to foodstuffs for particular nutritional uses, attribute to any foodstuff the property of preventing, treating or curing a human disease, or refer to such properties; Community provisions or, where there are none, national provisions may derogate from this rule in the case of natural mineral waters.

The procedure laid down in Article 16 shall apply to any such national provisions.

2. The Council, in accordance with the procedure laid down in Article 100 of the Treaty, shall draw up a non-exhaustive list of the claims within the meaning of paragraph 1, the use of which must at all events be prohibited or restricted.

3. The prohibitions or restrictions referred to in paragraphs 1 and 2 shall also apply to:

(a) the presentation of foodstuffs, in particular their shape, appearance or packaging, the packaging materials used, the way in which they are arranged and the setting in which they are displayed;

(b) advertising.

Article 3

1. In accordance with Articles 4 to 14 and subject to the exceptions contained therein, indication of the following particulars alone shall be compulsory on the labelling of foodstuffs:

(1) the name under which the product is sold,

(2) the list of ingredients,

(3) in the case of prepackaged foodstuffs, the net quantity,

(4) the date of minimum durability,

(5) any special storage conditions or conditions of use,

(6) the name or business name and address of the manufacturer or packager, or of a seller established within the Community.

However, the Member States shall be authorized, in respect of butter produced in their territory, to require only an indication of the manufacturer, packager or seller.

Without prejudice to the notification provided for in Article 22, Member States shall inform the Commission and the other Member States of any measure taken pursuant to this paragraph,

(7) particulars of the place of origin or provenance in the cases where failure to give such particulars might mislead the consumer to a material degree as to the true origin or provenance of the foodstuff.

(8) instructions for use when it would be impossible to make appropriate use of the foodstuff in the absence of such instructions.

2.   Notwithstanding the previous paragraph, Member States may retain national provisions which require indication of the factory or packaging centre, in respect of home production.

3.   The provisions of this Article shall be without prejudice to more precise or more extensive provisions regarding weights and measures.

Article 4

1.   Community provisions applicable to specified foodstuffs and not to foodstuffs in general may provide for derogations, in exceptional cases, from the requirements laid down in Article 3 (1), points 2 and 4, provided that this does not result in the purchaser being inadequately informed.

2.   Community provisions applicable to specified foodstuffs and not to foodstuffs in general may provide that other particulars in addition to those listed in Article 3 must appear on the labelling.

Where there are no Community provisions, Member States may make provision for such particulars in accordance with the procedure laid down in Article 16.

Article 5

1.   The name under which a foodstuff is sold shall be the name laid down by whatever laws, regulations or administrative provisions apply to the foodstuff in question or, in the absence of any such name, the name customary in the Member State where the product is sold to the ultimate consumer, or a description of the foodstuff and, if necessary, of its use, that is sufficiently precise to inform the purchaser of its true nature and to enable it to be distinguished from products with which it could be confused.

2.   No trade mark, brand name or fancy name may be substituted for the name under which the product is sold.

3.   The name under which the product is sold shall include or be accompanied by particulars as to the physical condition of the foodstuff or the specific treatment which it has undergone (e.g. powdered, freeze-dried, deep-frozen, concentrated, smoked) in all cases where omission of such information could create confusion in the mind of the purchaser.

Article 6

1.   Ingredients shall be listed in accordance with this Article and the Annexes.

2.   Ingredients need not be listed in the case of:

(a) — fresh fruit and vegetables, including potatoes, which have not been peeled, cut or similarly treated,

— carbonated water, the description of which indicates that it has been carbonated,

— fermentation vinegars derived exclusively from a single basic product, provided that no other ingredient has been added;

(b) — cheese,

— butter,

— fermented milk and cream,

provided that no ingredient has been added other than lactic products, enzymes and micro-organism cultures essential to manufacture, or the salt needed for the manufacture of cheese other than fresh cheese and processed cheese;

(c) products consisting of a single ingredient.

3.   In the case of beverages containing more than 1.2% by volume of alcohol, the Council, acting on a proposal from the Commission, shall, before the expiry of a period of four years following notification of this Directive, determine the rules for labelling ingredients and, possibly, indicating the alcoholic strength.

4. (a) 'Ingredient' shall mean any substance, including additives, used in the manufacture or preparation of a foodstuff and still present in the finished product, even if in altered form.

(b) Where an ingredient of the foodstuff is itself the product of several ingredients, the latter shall be regarded as ingredients of the foodstuff in question.

(c) The following shall not be regarded as ingredients:

(i) the constituents of an ingredient which have been temporarily separated during the manufacturing process and later reintroduced but not in excess of their original proportions:

(ii) — additives:

— whose presence in a given foodstuff is solely due to the fact that they were contained in one or more ingredients of that foodstuff, provided that they serve no technological function in the finished product,

— which are used as processing aids;

— substances used in the quantities strictly necessary as solvents or media for additives or flavouring.

(d) In certain cases Decisions may be taken in accordance with the procedure laid down in Article 17 as to whether the conditions described in (c) (ii) are satisfied.

5. (a) The list of ingredients shall include all the ingredients of the foodstuff, in descending order of weight, as recorded at the time of their use in the manufacture of the foodstuff. It shall appear preceded by a suitable heading which includes the word 'ingredients'.

However:

— added water and volatile products shall be listed in order of their weight in the finished product; the amount of water added as an ingredient in a foodstuff shall be calculated by deducting from the total amount of the finished product the total amount of the other ingredients used. This amount need not be taken into consideration if it does not exceed 5% by weight of the finished product;

— ingredients used in concentrated or dehydrated form and reconstituted at the time of manufacture may be listed in order of weight as recorded before their concentration or dehydration;

— in the case of concentrated or dehydrated foods which are intended to be reconstituted by the addition of water, the ingredients may be listed in order of proportion in the reconstituted product provided that the list of ingredients is accompanied by an expression such as 'ingredients of the reconstituted product', or 'ingredients of the ready-to-use product';

— in the case of mixtures of fruit or vegetables where no particular fruit or vegetable significantly predominates in proportion by weight, those ingredients may be listed in another order provided that that list of ingredients is accompanied by an expression such as 'in variable proportion';

— in the case of mixtures of spices or herbs, where none significantly predominates in proportion by weight, those ingredients may be listed in another order provided that that list of ingredients is accompanied by an expression such as 'in variable proportion';

(b) ingredients shall be designated by their specific name, where applicable, in accordance with the rules laid down in Article 5.

However:

— ingredients which belong to one of the categories listed in Annex I and are constituents of another foodstuff need only be designated by the name of that category;

— ingredients belonging to one of the categories listed in Annex II must be designated by the name of that category, followed by their specific name or EEC number; if an ingredient belongs to more than one of the categories, the category appropriate to the principal function in the case of the foodstuff in question shall be indicated; amendments to this Annex based on advances in scientific and technical knowledge shall be adopted in accordance with the procedure laid down in Article 17;

— flavouring matter shall be described in accordance with the national provisions applicable thereto, until the entry into force of the Community provisions;

— the Community provisions or, where there are none, the national provisions applicable to certain specified foodstuffs, many also provide for categories additional to those specified in Annex I. Without prejudice to the notification provided for in Article 22, Member States shall inform the Commission and the other Member States of any measure taken pursuant to this indent.

6. Community provisions or, where there are none, national provisions may lay down that the name under which a specific foodstuff is sold is to be accompanied by mention of a particular ingredient or ingredients.

The procedure laid down in Article 16 shall apply to any such national provisions.

7. In the case referred to in paragraph 4 (b), a compound ingredient may be included in the list of ingredients, under its own designation in so far as this is laid down by law or established by custom, in terms of its overall weight, provided that it is immediately followed by a list of its ingredients.

Such a list, however, shall not be compulsory:

— where the compound ingredient constitutes less than 25% of the finished product; however, this exemption shall not apply in the case of additives, subject to the provisions of paragraph 4 (c),

— where the compound ingredient is a foodstuff for which a list of ingredients is not required under Community rules.

8. Notwithstanding paragraph 5 (a), the water content need not be specified:

(a) where the water is used during the manufacturing process solely for the reconstitution of an ingredient used in concentrated or dehydrated form;

(b) in the case of a liquid medium which is not normally consumed.

Article 7

1. Where the labelling of a foodstuff places emphasis on the presence or low content of one or more ingredients which are essential to the specific properties of the foodstuff, or where the description of the foodstuff has the same effect, the minimum or maximum percentage, as the case may be, used in the manufacture thereof shall be stated.

This information shall appear either immediately next to the name under which the foodstuff is sold or in the list of ingredients in connection with the ingredient in question.

In accordance with the procedure laid down in Article 17, it may be decided that, in the case of certain ingredients, the percentage referred to in this paragraph shall be expressed in absolute terms.

2. Paragraph 1 shall not apply:

(a) in the case of labelling which is intended to characterize a foodstuff in accordance with Article 5(1) or which is required under Community provisions or, where there are none, under national provisions applicable to certain foodstuffs;

(b) in the case of ingredients used in small quantities only as flavourings.

3. Community provisions or, where there are none, national provisions may stipulate for certain foodstuffs, as well as in the case referred to in paragraph 2(a), that quantities of certain ingredients must be indicated either in absolute terms or as percentages and that, where appropriate, mention should be made of any alteration in the quantities of these ingredients.

The procedure laid down in Article 16 shall apply to any such national provisions.

Article 8

1. The net quantity of prepackaged foodstuffs shall be expressed:

—in units of volume in the case of liquids,

—in units of mass in the case of other products,

using the litre, centilitre, millilitre, kilogram or gram, as appropriate.

Community provisions or, where there are none, national provisions applicable to certain specified foodstuffs may derogate from this rule.

The procedure laid down in Article 16 shall apply to any such national provisions.

2. (a) Where the indication of a certain type of quantity (e.g. nominal quantity, minimum quantity, average quantity) is required by Community provisions or, where there are none, by national provisions, this quantity shall be regarded as the net quantity for the purposes of this Directive.

Without prejudice to the notification provided for in Article 22, Member States shall inform the Commission and the other Member States of any measure taken pursuant to this point.

(b) Community provisions or, where there are none, national provisions may, for certain specified foodstuffs classified by quantity in categories, require other indications of quantity.

The procedure laid down in Article 16 shall apply to any such national provisions.

(c) Where a prepackaged item consists of two or more individual prepackaged items containing the same quantity of the same product, the net quantity shall be indicated by mentioning the net quantity contained in each individual package and the total number of such packages. Indication of these particulars shall not, however, be compulsory where the total number of individual packages can be clearly seen and easily counted from the outside and where at least one indication of the net quantity contained in each individual package can be clearly seen from the outside.

(d) Where a prepackaged item consists of two or more individual packages which are not regarded as units of sale, the net quantity shall be given by indicating the total net quantity and the total number of individual packages. Community provisions or, where there are none, national provisions need not, in the case of certain foodstuffs, require indication of the total number of individual packages.

Without prejudice to the notification provided for in Article 22, Member States shall inform the Commission and the other Member States of any measure taken pursuant to this point.

3. In the case of foodstuffs normally sold by number, Member States need not require indication of the net quantity provided that the number of items can clearly be seen and easily counted from the outside or, if not, is indicated on the labelling.

Without prejudice to the notification provided for in Article 22, Member States shall inform the Commission and the other Member States of any measure taken pursuant to this paragraph.

4. Where a solid foodstuff is presented in a liquid medium, the drained net weight of the foodstuff shall also be indicated on the labelling.

For the purposes of this paragraph, 'liquid medium' shall mean the following products, possibly in mixtures, provided that the liquid is merely an adjunct to the essential elements of that preparation and is thus not a decisive factor for the purchase: water, salt water, brine, vinegar, aqueous solutions of sugars, and fruit or vegetable juices in the case of tinned fruit or vegetables.

Methods of checking the drained net weight shall be determined in accordance with the procedure laid down in Article 17.

5. It shall not be compulsory to indicate the net quantity in the case of foodstuffs:

(a) which are subject to considerable losses in their volume or mass and which are sold by number or weighed in the presence of the purchaser;

(b) the net quantity of which is less than 5 g or 5 ml; however, this provision shall not apply to spices and herbs.

Community provisions or, where there are none, national provisions applicable to specified foodstuffs may in exceptional cases lay down thresholds which are higher than 5 g or 5 ml provided that this does not result in the purchaser being inadequately informed.

Without prejudice to the notification provided for in Article 22, Member States shall inform the Commission and the other Member States of any measure taken pursuant to this paragraph.

6. Until the end of the transitional period during which the use of the imperial units of measurement contained in Chapter D of the Annex to Directive 71/354/EEC of 18 October 1971 on the approximation of the laws of the Member States relating to units of measurement[1], as last amended by Directive 76/770/EEC[2], is authorized in the Community, Ireland and the United Kingdom may permit the quantity to be expressed only in imperial units of measurement calculated on the basis of the following conversion rates:

—1 ml = 0.0352 fluid ounces,

—1 l = 1.760 pints or 0.220 gallons,

—1 g = 0.0353 ounces (avoirdupois),

—1 kg = 2.205 pounds.

Article 9

1. The date of minimum durability of a foodstuff shall be the date until which the foodstuff retains its specific properties when properly stored.

It shall be indicated in accordance with the provisions of this Article.

[1]OJ No L 243, 29.10.1971, p.29.
[2]OJ No L 262, 27.9.1976, p.204.

2. The date shall be preceded by the words:

—'Best before . . .' when the date includes an indication of the day,

—'Best before end . . .' in other cases.

However, in the case of certain foodstuffs which, from the micro-biological point of view, are highly perishable, Member States may require the words 'use before: . . .' to be indicated. Without prejudice to the notification provided for in Article 22, Member States shall inform the Commission and the other Member States of any measure taken pursuant to this subparagraph.

Before the expiry of a period of six years from the date of notification of this Directive, the Council, acting on a proposal from the Commission, shall decide on the common date-indication arrangements for highly perishable foodstuffs of the sort referred to in the second subparagraph.

3. The words referred to in paragraph 2 shall be accompanied by:

—either the date itself, or

—a reference to where the date is given on the labelling.

If need be, these particulars shall be followed by a description of the storage conditions which must be observed if the product is to keep for the specified period.

4. The date shall consist of the day, month and year in uncoded chronological form.

However, in the case of foodstuffs:

—which will not keep for more than three months, an indication of the day and the month will suffice,

—which will keep for more than three months but not more than 18 months, an indication of the month and year will suffice,

—which will keep for more than 18 months, an indication of the year will suffice.

The manner of indicating the date may be specified according to the procedure laid down in Article 17.

5. In their own territories the Member States may permit the minimum durability period to be expressed otherwise than in terms of the date of minimum durability.

Without prejudice to the notification provided for in Article 22, Member States shall notify the Commission and the other Member States of any measure taken under this paragraph.

6. Subject to the Community provisions governing the products below, an indication of the date of minimum durability shall not be required for:

—fresh fruit and vegetables, including potatoes, which have not been peeled, cut or similarly treated,

—wines, liqueur wines, sparkling wines, aromatized wines, fruit wines and sparkling fruit wines,

—beverages containing 10% or more by volume of alcohol,

—bakers' or pastry-cooks' wares which, given the nature of their content, are normally consumed within 24 hours of their manufacture,

—vinegar,

—cooking salt,

—solid sugar,

—confectionery products consisting of flavoured and/or coloured sugars.

Article 10

1. The instructions for use of a foodstuff shall be indicated in such a way as to enable appropriate use to be made thereof.

2. Community provisions or, where there are none, national provisions may, in the case of certain foodstuffs, specify the way in which the instructions for use should be indicated.

The procedure laid down in Article 16 shall apply to such national provisions.

Article 11

1. (a) When the foodstuffs are prepackaged, the particulars

provided for in Article 3 and Article 4(2) shall appear on the prepackaging or on a label attached thereto.

(b) Notwithstanding point (a) and without prejudice to Community provisions on nominal amounts, Member States may authorize that all or some of the particulars provided for in Article 3 and Article 4(2) be given only on the relevant trade documents when the foodstuffs are prepackaged and marketed prior to their sale to the ultimate consumer.

Without prejudice to the notification provided for in Article 22, Member States shall inform the Commission and the other Member States of any measure taken pursuant to this point.

The Council, acting on a proposal from the Commission, shall lay down the provisions to apply subsequently in this connection not later than nine years after notification of this Directive.

2. These particulars shall be easy to understand and marked in a conspicuous place in such a way as to be easily visible, clearly legible and indelible.

They shall not in any way be hidden, obscured or interrupted by other written or pictorial matter.

3. (a) The particulars listed in Article 3(1), points 1, 3 and 4, shall appear in the same field of vision.

This requirement may be extended to the particulars provided for in Article 4(2).

(b) However, for glass bottles intended for re-use, upon which one of the particulars listed in point (a) is indelibly marked, this requirement shall not apply for a period of 10 years following notification of this Directive.

4. Member States may:

(a) permit that only the particulars listed in Article 3(1), points 1, 3 and 4, be indicated on packaging or containers the largest surface of which has an area of less than 10 cm^2,

(b) require the indication of only some of the particulars listed in Article 3 in respect of milk or milk products in bottles intended for re-use; in this case they may also provide for derogations from paragraph 3(a).

Without prejudice to the notification provided for in Article 22, Member States shall inform the Commission and the other Member States of any measure taken pursuant to this paragraph.

Article 12

Where foodstuffs are offered for sale to the ultimate consumer without prepackaging, or where foodstuffs are packaged on the sales premises at the consumer's request or prepackaged for direct sale, the Member States shall adopt detailed rules concerning the manner in which the particulars specified in Article 3 and Article 4(2) are to be shown.

They may decide not to require the provision of all or some of these particulars, provided that the consumer still receives sufficient information.

Article 13

This Directive shall not affect the provisions of national laws which, in the absence of Community provisions, impose less stringent requirements for the labelling of foodstuffs presented in fancy packaging such as figurines or souvenirs.

Article 14

Member States shall refrain from laying down requirements more detailed than those already contained in Articles 3 to 11 concerning the manner in which the particulars provided for in Article 3 and Article 4(2) are to be shown.

The Member States shall, however, ensure that the sale of foodstuffs within their own territories is prohibited if the particulars provided in Article 3 and Article 4(2) do not appear in a language easily understood by purchasers, unless other measures have been taken to ensure that the purchaser is informed. This provision shall not prevent such particulars from being indicated in various languages.

Article 15

1. Member States may not forbid trade in foodstuffs which comply with the rules laid down in this Directive by the application of non-harmonized national provisions governing the labelling and presentation of certain foodstuffs or of foodstuffs in general.

2. Paragraph 1 shall not apply to non-harmonized national provisions justified on grounds of:

—protection of public health,

—prevention of fraud, unless such provisions are liable to impede the application of the definitions and rules laid down by this Directive,

—protection of industrial and commercial property rights, indications of provenance, registered designations of origin and prevention of unfair competition.

Article 16

Where reference is made to this Article, the following procedure shall apply:

(1) When a Member State maintains the provisions of its national laws, it shall inform the Commission and the other Member States thereof within a period of two years after notification of this Directive;

(2) Should a Member State deem it necessary to adopt new legislation, it shall notify the Commission and the other Member States of the measures envisaged and give the reasons justifying them. The Commission shall consult the Member States within the Standing Committee on Foodstuffs if it considers such consultation to be useful or if a Member State so requests.

Member States may take such envisaged measures only three months after such notification and provided that the Commission's opinion is not negative.

In the latter event, and before the expiry of the abovementioned period, the Commission shall initiate the procedure provided for in Article 17 in order to determine whether the envisaged measures may be implemented subject, if necessary, to the appropriate modifications.

Article 17

1. Where the procedure laid down in this Article is invoked, the matter shall be referred to the Standing Committee on Foodstuffs (hereinafter called 'the Committee') by its chairman, either on his own initiative or at the request of a representative of a Member State.

2. The representative of the Commission shall submit to the Committee a draft of the measures to be taken. The Committee shall give its opinion on that draft within a time limit set by the chairman having regard to the urgency of the matter. Opinions shall be delivered by a majority of 41 votes, the votes of the Member States being weighted as provided for in Article 148(2) of the Treaty. The chairman shall not vote.

3. (a) Where the measures envisaged are in accordance with the opinion of the Committee, the Commission shall adopt them.

(b) Where the measures envisaged are not in accordance with the opinion of the Committee, or if no opinion is delivered, the Commission shall without delay submit to the Council a proposal on the measures to be taken. The Council shall act by a qualified majority.

(c) If the Council has not acted within three months of the proposal being submitted to it, the proposed measures shall be adopted by the Commission.

Article 18

Article 17 shall apply for 18 months from the date on which the matter was first referred to the Committee pursuant to Article 17.

Article 19

If temporary measures prove necessary to facilitate the application of this Directive, they shall be adopted in accordance with the procedure provided for in Article 17.

Article 20

This Directive shall not affect Community provisions relating to the labelling and presentation of certain foodstuffs already adopted at the time of its notification.

Any amendments necessary to harmonize such provisions with the rules laid down in this Directive shall be decided in accordance with the procedure applicable to each of the provisions in question.

Article 21

This Directive shall not apply to products for export outside the Community.

Article 22

1. Member States shall make such amendments to their laws as may be necessary to comply with the provisions of this Directive and shall forthwith inform the Commission thereof; the laws thus amended shall be applied in such a way as to:

—permit trade in those products which

comply with the provisions of this Directive no later than two years after its notification,

—prohibit trade in those products which do not comply with the provisions of this Directive four years after its notification.

2. However, Member States may:

(a) in the case of certain foodstuffs, reduce the period specified in the second indent of paragraph 1;

(b) in the case of certain foodstuffs which keep for a long time, extend the period specified in the second indent of paragraph 1;

(c) without prejudice to the first indent of Article 23(1)(b), in the case of foodstuffs which will keep for more than 12 months, extend to six years the period laid down in the second indent of paragraph 1 above as regards the obligation to indicate the date of minimum durability.

3. In the case referred to:

(a) in paragraph 2(a), the procedure laid down in Article 16(2) shall apply to any national provision;

(b) in paragraph 2(b) and (c), Member States shall inform the Commission and the other Member States of any measure taken pursuant to the said points.

4. Member States shall also ensure that the Commission receives the text of any essential provision of national law which they adopt in the field governed by this Directive.

Article 23

1. By way of derogation from the second indent of Article 22(1), Member States may make implementation of the provisions relating to the following matters optional:

(a) the designation, provided for in the second indent of Article 6(5)(b), of the specific name or EEC number of the ingredients belonging to one of the categories listed in Annex II;

(b) the indication provided for in

Article 9, of the date of minimum durability in the case of:

—foodstuffs whose minimum durability exceeds 18 months,

—deep-frozen foodstuffs,

—ice-creams,

—chewing gums and similar chewing products,

—fermented cheese intended to ripen completely or partially in prepackaging;

(c) the information provided for in Annex I to supplement the designation 'oil' or 'fat'.

2. Without prejudice to the information provided for in Article 22, Member States shall inform the Commission and the other Member States of any measure taken pursuant to paragraph 1.

3. After a period of five years following notification of this Directive, the Council shall, in accordance with the procedure laid down in Article 100 of the Treaty, decide upon the common rules to apply in the cases referred to in paragraph 1.

Article 24

This Directive shall also apply to the French overseas departments.

Article 25

This Directive shall not apply to foodstuffs marketed in Greenland, intended for local consumption.

Article 26

This Directive is addressed to the Member States.

Done at Brussels, 18 December 1978.

For the Council

The President

J. ERTL

ANNEX I

Categories of ingredients which may be designated by the name of the category rather than the specific name

Definition	*Designation*
Refined oils other than olive oil.	'Oil', together with —either the adjective 'vegetable' or 'animal', as appropriate, or —an indication of their specific vegetable or animal origin. The adjective 'hydrogenated' must accompany the indication of a hydrogenated oil where the vegetable origin or the specific vegetable or animal origin is mentioned. However, in either case, Member States may lay down requirements which are more stringent in the case of foodstuffs consisting essentially of oils and fats, emulsified sauces or preparations where the oil serves as a liquid medium; in that case the procedure laid down in Article 16 shall apply.

Definition	*Designation*
Refined fats.	'Fat', together with —either the adjective 'vegetable' or 'animal', as appropriate, or —an indication of their specific vegetable or animal origin. However, in either case, Member States may lay down requirements which are more stringent in the case of foodstuffs consisting essentially of oils and fats or emulsified sauces; in that case the procedure laid down in Article 16 shall apply.
Mixtures of flour obtained from two or more cereal species.	'Flour', followed by a list of the cereals from which it has been obtained in descending order by weight.
Starches, and starches modified by physical or enzymatic means.	Starch.
All species of fish where the fish constitutes an ingredient of another foodstuff and provided that the name and presentation of such foodstuff does not refer to a specific species of fish.	Fish.
All types of poultrymeat where such meat constitutes an ingredient of another foodstuff and provided that the name and presentation of such a foodstuff does not refer to a specific type of poultrymeat.	Poultrymeat.
All types of cheese where the cheese or mixture of cheeses constitutes an ingredient of another foodstuff and provided that the name and presentation of such foodstuff does not refer to a specific type of cheese.	Cheese.
All spices and spice extracts not exceeding 2% by weight of the foodstuff.	Spice(s) or mixed spices.
All herbs or parts of herbs not exceeding 2% by weight of the foodstuff.	Herb(s) or mixed herbs.
All types of gum preparations used in the manufacture of gum base for chewing gum.	Gum base.
All types of crumbed baked cereal products.	Crumbs or rusks as appropriate.
All types of sucrose.	Sugar.

14

Definition	*Designation*
Anhydrous dextrose and dextrose mono-hydrate.	Dextrose.
All types of caseinates.	Caseinates.
Press, expeller or refined cocoa butter.	Cocoa butter.
All crystallized fruit not exceeding 10% of the weight of the foodstuff.	Crystallized fruit.

ANNEX II

Categories of ingredients which must be designated by the name of the category to which they belong, followed by their specific name or EEC number

Colour

Preservative

Antioxidant

Emulsifier

Thickener

Gelling agent

Stabilizer

Flavour enhancer

Acid

Acidity regulator

Anticaking agent

Modified starches[1]

Artificial sweetener

Raising agent

Antifoaming agent

Glazing agent

Emulsifying salts[2]

Flour improvers

---

[1] Indication of specific name or EEC number is not required.
[2] Only for processed cheeses and processed cheese products.

APPENDIX 4

REVISED SCHEDULE OF FISH NAMES

NOTE: As referred to in paragraph 218 (c), *names in brackets* should only be permitted in association with the first name listed. The use of names in brackets is however optional where the first name is already given.

Appropriate Designation	Species
SEA FISH	
1. Anchovy	All species of *Engraulis*
2. Bass	*Dicentrarchus labrax*
3. Brill	*Scophthalmus rhombus* (L.)
4. Brisling	Canned *Sprattus sprattus* (L.)
5. Catfish (Rockfish)	All species of *Anarhichas*
6. Cod or Codling	*Gadus Morhua* (L.)
7. Coley (Saithe) (Coalfish)	*Pollachius virens* (L.)
8. Conger	All species of *Conger*
9. Dab	*Limanda limanda* (L.)
10. Dogfish (Flake) (Huss) (Rigg)	All species of *Galeorhinus* All species of *Mustelus* All species of *Scyliorhinus* *Galeus melastomus* (Rafin.) *Squalus acanthias* (L.)
11. Dory (John Dory)	*Zeus faber* (L.)
12. Eel	All species of *Anguilla*
13. Flounder	*Platichthys flesus* (L.)
14. Forkbeard	All species of *Phycis* All species of *Urophycis* *Raniceps raninus* (L.)
15. Garfish	All species of *Belone*
16. Grey Mullet	All species of *Mugil* All species of *Liza* All species of *Chelon*
17. Gurnard	All genera of Triglidae *Peristedion cataphractum* (L.)
18. Haddock	*Melanogrammus aeglefinus* (L.)
19. Hake	*Merluccius merluccius* (L.)
20. Cape Hake	*Merluccius capensis* (Castelnau) *Merluccius paradoxus* (Franca)
21. Atlantic Hake	*Merluccius hubbsi* (Marini) *Merluccius bilinearis* (Mitchell)
22. Pacific Hake	*Merluccius productus* (Ayres) *Merluccius gayi* (Guich)
23. Halibut	*Hippoglossus hippoglossus* (L.)
24. Black Halibut (Greenland Halibut)	*Reinhardtius hippoglossoides* (Walbaum)
25. Herring	*Clupea harengus* (L.)
26. Lascar	*Pegusa lascaris* (Risso)
27. Ling	All species of *Molva*
28. Mackerel	All species of *Scomber*
29. Megrim	All species of *Lepidorhombus*

1

Appropriate Designation	Species
30. Monkfish (Angler)	*Lophius piscatorius* (L.)
31. Pilchard	*Sardina pilchardus* (Walbaum)
32. Pacific Pilchard	{ *Sardinops sagax caerulea* (Girard) *Sardinops sagax sagax* (Jenyns) *Sardinops sagax melanosticta* (Schlegel)
33. South Atlantic Pilchard	*Sardinops sagax ocellata* (Pappe)
34. Plaice	*Pleuronectes platessa* (L.)
35. Pollack (Lythe)	*Pollachius pollachius* (L.)
36. Pacific Pollack (Alaska Pollack)	*Theragra chalcogrammus*
37. Pout (Pouting)	*Trisopterus luscus* (L.)
38. Redfish (Ocean Perch) (Rose Fish)	{ All species of *Sebastes* *Helicolenus maculatus* *Helicolenus dactylopterus* (De la Roche)
39. Red Mullet	All species of *Mullus*
40. Roughback	*Hippoglossoides platessoides* (Fabr.)
41. Sardine	Small *Sardina pilchardus* (Walbaum)
42. Sardinella	All species of *Sardinella*
43. Scad	All species of *Trachurus*
44. Sea Bream	All genera of Sparidae
45. Sild	{ Canned small *Clupea harengus* (L.) Canned small *Sprattus sprattus* (L.)
46. Skate (Ray) (Roker)	All species of *Raja*
47. Smelt (Sparling)	All species of *Osmerus*
48. Sole (Dover Sole)	*Solea solea* (L.)
49. Canary Sole	*Solea senegalensis*
50. Lemon Sole	*Microstomus kitt* (Walbaum)
51. Sprat	*Sprattus sprattus* (L.) (other than canned)
52. Thickback	*Microchirus variegatus* (Don.)
53. Tuna (Tunny)	{ All species of *Thunnus* except *Thunnus alalunga* (Bonnaterre) All species of *Neothunnus*
54. Albacore Tuna	*Thunnus alalunga* (Bonnaterre)
55. Bonito Tuna	All species of *Sarda*
56. Skipjack Tuna	{ All species of *Euthynnus* *Katsuwonus pelamis* (L.)
57. Turbot	*Scophthalmus maximus* (L.)
58. Tusk	*Brosme brosme* (Ascanius)
59. Whitebait	{ Small *Clupea harengus* (L.) Small *Sprattus sprattus* (L.) } Other than canned
60. Whiting	*Merlangius merlangus* (L.) }
61. Blue Whiting	*Micromesistius poutassou*
62. Winter Flounder	*Pseudopleuronectes americanus* (Walbaum)
63. Witch	*Glyptocephalus cynoglossus* (L.)

SALMON AND FRESHWATER FISH

1. Salmon*	*Salmo salar* (L.)
2. Cherry Salmon*	*Oncorhynchus masou* (Walbaum)
3. Chum Salmon or Keta Salmon*	*Onchorhyncus keta* (Walbaum)
4. Medium Red Salmon or Coho Salmon or Silver Salmon*	*Oncorhynchus kisutch* (Walbaum)

*When sold smoked, these names must be used as appropriate preceded by 'smoked'.

Appropriate Designation	Species
5. Pink Salmon*	*Oncorhynchus gorbuscha* (Walbaum)
6. Red Salmon or Sockeye Salmon*	*Oncorhynchus nerka* (Walbaum)
7. Spring Salmon or King Salmon or Chinook Salmon*	*Oncorhynchus tschwytscha* (Walbaum)
8. Brown Trout	*Salmo trutta* (L.) which has spent all of its life in fresh water
9. Sea Trout (Salmon Trout)	*Salmo trutta* (L.) which has spent part of its life in sea water
10. Cut-throat Trout	*Salmo clarkii* (Richardson)
11. Rainbow Trout (Steelhead Trout)	*Salmo gairdneri* (Richardson)

*When sold smoked, these names must be used as appropriate preceded by 'smoked'.

SHELLFISH

Name	Species
1. Abalone (Ormer)	All species of *Haliotis*
2. Clam or Hard Shell Clam	*Mercenaria mercenaria* (L.) *Venus verrucosa* (L.)
3. Clam or Razor Clam	All species of *Ensis* and *Solen*
4. Cockle	All species of *Cerastoderma*
5. Crab	All species of the section Brachyura All species of the family Lithodidae
6. Crawfish (Spiny Lobster) (Rock Lobster)	All species of the family Palinuridae
7. Crayfish	All species of the family Astacidae All species of the family Parastacidae All species of the family Austroastacidae
8. Lobster	All species of *Homarus*
9. Slipper Lobster	All species of *Scyllaridae*
10. Squat Lobster	All species of the family *Galatheidae*
11. Mussel	All species of *Mytilus*
12. Oyster	All species of *Crassostrea* except *Crassostrea angulata* (Lmk.) and *Crassostrea gigas* All species of *Ostrea* except *Ostrea edulis* (L.)
13. Oyster or Portuguese Oyster	*Crassostrea angulata* (Lmk.)
14. Oyster or Pacific Oyster	*Crassostrea gigas*
15. Oyster or Native Oyster	*Ostrea edulis* (L.)
16. Prawn	*Fish with a count of 330/kg (150/lb) or less peeled, cooked tails of: All species of *Palaemonidae* All species of *Penaeidae* All species of *Pandalidae*
17. Scallop	All species of *Pectinidae*
18. Scallop or Queen Scallop (Queen)	*Chlamys (Acquipecton) opercularis* (L.)

3

Name	Species
19. Scampi (Norway Lobster) (Dublin Bay Prawn)	*Nephrops norvegicus* (L.)
20. Shrimp or Pink Shrimp	*Pandalus montagui* (Leach)
21. Shrimp or Brown Shrimp	All species of *Crangon*
22. Shrimp	*Fish with a count of more than 330/kg (150/lb) peeled, cooked tails of:
	All species of *Palaemonidae*
	All species of *Penaeidae*
	All species of *Pandalidae*
23. Whelk	All species of *Buccinum*
24. Winkle	All species of *Littorina*

*For whole prawns and shrimps corresponding limits to those given for peeled cooked tails above to be determined and included.

APPENDIX 5

EEC RESTRICTIONS ON THE USE OF THE WORD 'WINE'

*EEC REGULATION 355/79
(OJ L 54, 5.3.79, p.99)

*EEC REGULATION 1608/76
(OJ L 183, 8.7.76, p.1)

Article 45

1. The appellation:
   (a) 'Wine' shall be restricted to products conforming to the definition given in part 8 of Annex II to Regulation (EEC) No. 337/79;
   (b) 'Table wine' shall be restricted to products conforming to the definition given in point 11 of that Annex.

2. Without prejudice to the provisions for the harmonisation of laws, the possibility for the Member States to allow:
   — the use of the word 'wine' accompanied by the name of a fruit and in the form of a composite name to describe products obtained by the fermentation of fruits other than grapes,
   — other composite names including the word 'wine', shall not, however, be affected by the provisions of paragraph 1.
In the event of use of the composite names referred to in the previous subparagraph, any confusion with the products referred to in paragraph 1 must be avoided.

Article 20

1. Pursuant to Article 45 (2) of Regulation (EEC) No. 355/79 (previously Article 44 (2) of Regulation (EEC) No. 2133/74) Member States may authorise, to describe either beverages from their own production or beverages which originate in other Member States or which have been imported, the use of the word 'wine':
   (a) in conjunction with the name of a fruit falling within Chapter 8 of the Common Customs Tariff, provided that such beverage was obtained by an alcoholic fermentation of that fruit; or
   (b) in composite names such as:
      — British wine or
      — Irish wine.

2. To avoid confusion between the terms referred to in paragraph 1 above and the words 'wine' and 'table wine', Member States shall ensure that:
   — the word 'wine' is used only in a composite name and in no circumstances on its own, and
   — the composite names referred to in the first indent are shown on the label in lettering of the same type and the same colour and of such a height that they are clearly distinguishable from other information.

*These Regulations lay down rules for the description and presentation of wines and grape musts.

Printed in England for Her Majesty's Stationery Office by Robendene Ltd, Amersham
Dd 597196/007192 K36 9/79.